THE SHERLOCK HOLMES PUZZLE BOOK

THE
SHERLOCK HOLMES
PUZZLE BOOK

173 Original Crosswords, Double-Crostics, Mazes and Other Brain Teasers

A Puzzler's Companion to the Sherlock Holmes Adventures

by
Dale Copps

A Doubleday/Dolphin Book

Doubleday & Company, Inc.   Garden City, New York

ISBN: 0-385-14839-9
Library of Congress Catalog Card Number
Copyright © 1981 by Dale Copps
Design by Douglas Wink
Manufactured in the United States of America
First Edition

Dedicated
to
the memory
of
Robert Carroll White
and
to
Julian Wolff
Commissionaire
of
The Baker Street Irregulars

THE RULES OF THE GAME –
A Necessary Introduction

I had a great time writing this book.

In the summer of 1978, a good friend of mine (Hi, Joe!) fled his seaside apartment in New Jersey for more spartan surroundings, to work on his doctoral thesis. I moved in with my dog, PG, an unabridged dictionary, a ream of graph paper and my old, two-volume Doubleday edition of the Canon. While my friends in New York sweltered through another summer, I basked in the eternal sun an hour or two every day and, for the rest, became immersed in "the half-remembered, half-forgotten times of snug Victorian illusion," as the great Sherlockian Edgar Smith described the world of our Master.

It was good to be enjoying, for the third time, a steady diet of Holmes and Watson. The first time I had done so, when I was eleven or twelve and just discovering Holmes, I was thrilled by the evil characters, the excitement, the danger, the women—frail or bold—and most of all by the Master's uncanny powers.

Four years ago I was immersed again, writing my Holmes quiz book (now, alas, out of print). At that time, I was attracted by the richness of the Canon, by the sheer numbers of characters, places, crimes, motives and solutions. I noted the themes as well—of passion, of revenge, of order and chaos, of a pure evil against a goodness that rose above the law and the crabbed morality of its own time.

During this, my third Holmesian immersion, plop in the middle of a period when I am eager to stay out of work by writing—more, better and quicker—I was particularly attracted to the language of the Canon: the simplicity and precision of Watson's vocabulary; the elegance of the long sentences so artfully balanced; the metaphor; the robustness; and overall, the humor. No need to quote examples here. There are a couple hundred in the book you are about to participate in and, I sincerely hope, enjoy as much as I have enjoyed its composition.

Speaking of the book, here are a few precepts in thy memory, entitled, "Why the Book Should Be Done in Order":

1. It's my first puzzle book, and for that I don't make apologies, but I did it in the order presented here, and it *does* get better as it goes along.

2. The order is identical to the order in the only established, definitive American edition of Holmes, *The Complete Sherlock Holmes*, published by Doubleday and Company, and none other.

3. Some puzzles require confronting only after you've gotten other, preceding puzzles under your belt.

4. The puzzles are numbered from 1 to 173, and you *know* Holmes would proceed one step at a time, so who are you to go slogging into the middle of things, disrupting my symmetry?

The answers are also numbered and may be found in the back of the book.

Finally, what better way to revisit that tattered old Holmes, or crack the new one you got for Christmas, than page by page from "The Study in Scarlet" right on down to "The Adventure of the Retired Colourman"? Many references to the Canon throughout the book are followed by a number in parentheses. This number refers to the page in the complete Doubleday edition of Holmes where the reference may be found. The page numbers offer the puzzler a "leg up" should the memory falter. One puzzle requires the Doubleday edition for completion. Otherwise, any complete edition will do, such as *The Annotated Sherlock Holmes* (if you can afford it), or the British edition (if you can find it). The Ballantine edition is *not* complete.

There are one to six pages devoted to each story. If I have slighted your favorites, write me and I'll make up for it in Volume II (which I'll compose if I get enough letters to persuade Doubleday to do a sequel; if I don't, then tough). I weighted puzzle distribution largely to my own preferences, and somewhat to the exigencies of laying out a book of this sort. The latter consideration, together with some faulty planning on my part, necessitated slighting "Hound of the Baskervilles," one of the finest tales, and overly favoring "The Valley of Fear," not among my favorites in the Canon.

There are sixteen varieties of puzzles in this book, the directions for many of which · are not in my introductory comments on each puzzle. So here's a necessary word or two about them:

Crosswords. (The first example is Puzzle #1.) I apologize for the occasional (well, actually rather frequent) fanciful abbreviations and repetitions of entries you'll encounter. I recommend to all budding crossword creators Una Merkel, Amon Ra and the SST. Holmes and Watson are abbreviated H and W throughout most definitions.

Double-Crostics. (First example, Puzzle #2) In this one, you solve as many of the clues as you can, filling in the answers in the numbered spaces provided, then transferring the letters to the numbered boxes on the grid. As words begin to form on the grid, you can work backward, completing them on the grid and filling in letters in the clues. Clue letters are provided in the grid spaces for each reference. The quotations in the grids are all from the story being dealt with in that puzzle, as are any Holmesian references in the clues. (The same, I might add, is true for all puzzles in the book, except the Codes.) The clue line—the first letter of each answer entry in the clues—is a *second* quotation from the story, contrasting or complementing the main one.

Mazes. (First example, Puzzle #3) Directions accompany these.

Quotations. (First example, Puzzle #4) I really enjoy these simple little puzzles. Quotations are wonderfully simple to create. I take a line from the story and write it out in a grid, consisting usually of four lines, each containing twelve to fifteen characters, letters or spaces. Then I drop all the letters in each vertical line, alphabetized, below

the puzzle, and you have to put them back in correct order.

Word Detections. (First example, Puzzle #9) These are like the "Word Finds" you see all over the place. The leftover letters in most of them reveal a "Mystery Quotation" from the story.

Diagramless. (First example, Puzzle #12) This is a crossword without the blanks provided. Clues are usually easier and words shorter. You can discover the starting box (always on the first horizontal line) either by a maddening effusion of patience and industry or by turning to the last answer page, where you'll find them listed. The puzzles are all diagonally symmetrical, so any blanks you begin to fill in at the start can be filled in in their diagonal opposites as well.

Hidden Phrases. (First example, Puzzle #13) A Word Detection grid with whole sentences to find. Usually there are two entries, sometimes only one. Letter counts are provided for most. Hint: Find the longest word and work back and forward from it. Individual words are always in a straight line. The end of one word usually abuts the next horizontally, vertically or diagonally, though sometimes the last letter of one word is the first of the next. Other overlappings occur when words come circling around to cross one another.

Semi-Crostics. (First example, Puzzle #14) Answer the definitions and fill in the resulting letters in the solution spaces, much as in a Double-Crostic. There is no second quotation, however, and some letters in the definition answers—those that are in boldface type—are repeated in other answers. This puzzle and others develop variations later in the book—yet another reason for doing them in order.

Cryptic-Quizzes. (First example, Puzzle #17) These are lists of people, places or things from our tales, translated into cryptogram, or alphabet-substitution code. If you're put off by the look of these, or the cryptograms, read "The Adventure of the Dancing Men," for hints on how to solve them.

Scramblegrams. (First example, Puzzle #20) In this puzzle I take either one sentence and rearrange its words or two sentences and interweave them (without altering the order of words in each sentence). You have to either unscramble one sentence or unlink the two sentences.

Cryptograms. (First example, Puzzle #21) These are quotations solved in the same manner as Cryptic-Quizzes.

Kriss Kross. (Puzzle #29) Only one. Having cursed my way through it, I didn't think the form worth the considerable effort of creating, compared to the questionable gratification of solving.

Anagrams. (First example, Puzzle #36) These are probably more fun to create than to solve, and are not well suited to a thematic puzzle book, where if you haven't read the story the solution is impossible, and if you have, it's too simple. Directions accompany.

Specials. There are two special puzzles I have created, with directions accompanying them. I don't fancy they'll attain puzzle immortality, but they do offer a change of pace.

Codes. Codes are codes, and there they sit when you encounter

them, challenging you to find the key to their secret treasures, which are all comments directly from me to you. They're all solvable, so don't go running to the answer section prematurely. Many took me an hour or two to be satisfied with, and some may take you that long to solve.

I suggest you attempt all the puzzles *before* reading the stories. Some will be impossible. Some will merely be extra challenging. Others will be easier and should whet your appetite for the tale involved.

A final word about the inception of this book. It wasn't my idea, but rather that of a young man named Robert Carroll White. He worked long and hard on the book. It was, with him, a real labor of love. One day, in the middle of his work, he had a heart attack and died. Doubleday sought a replacement and found and chose me, on a recommendation from Dr. Julian Wolff of the Baker Street Irregulars, the first and foremost Sherlockian society in America. Dr. Wolff knew of my quiz book.

Very little of Mr. White's work was finished enough to include in this book, but some of it was, and it's among the finest work here. Proper credit has been given throughout.

I hope Mr. White is pleased with what became, for me as well, a labor of love.

Ocean City, N.J.
New York City

The Sherlock Holmes Puzzle Book

A Study in Scarlet

1. In which the world is introduced to the Master and his Boswell. We commemorate the event with our largest crossword puzzle.

ACROSS

1 The bullet that shattered W's shoulder (15)
7 Drebber's was poison (81)
11 Brazilian city, for short
14 W preferred coffee to this
17 Portuguese port
18 Where W often ends up trying to match wits with II
19 Subordinate, helper: abbr.
20 Skin tumor, usually on the scalp
21 W was appalled at H's ignorance of this: 3 wds.
24 The law is this, according to Beadle Bumble
25 Drebber probably occasionally suffered from these: Abbr.
26 ". . . he was as sensitive to flattery on the _____ of his art as any girl could be of her beauty" (34)
27 Peck; pat
30 French business abbreviation
31 The contented Borden cow
35 "There has been a _____ business during the night" (26)
38 29 Down is one
39 Fusses
41 Greek porch
42 Eggs, to Caesar
43 A Kennedy
44 A particularly foul disease: Abbr.
45 Exclamations, or a homonym of the Emerald City
48 Picnic pest
49 Some that H visited were definitely "of iniquity"
51 The eighties, for instance
53 An earlier pretender to H's glory (24)
54 German Santa
56 Hold the roll!: 2 wds.
57 Another English brew little heard of at 221B
58 Monogram of Little Bighorn loser
61 "Helen, thy beauty _____": Poe, 3 wds.
63 In blood-red letters on the wall at 3 Lauriston Gardens (31)
65 Good name for a little darling
67 Born: Fr.
68 Disclose, to a poet
70 The whalebones in Victorian corsets
72 Brothers to 35 Down
73 "I have my eye on a suite in _____ Street" (19)
74 The endangered cats of India
76 Jacob's brother
77 "The _____ Corbies"
79 Big foot?
80 Shad _____
81 "You're the _____": Porter melody
83 Wave: Span.
84 Knows: Scot.
86 _____ Fein: Irish society not unlike 37 Down
87 Collection of anecdotes
88 H's knowledge of Literature, Philosophy and Astronomy
89 As Lewis Carroll might say, curiouser
91 "It was rare for him to be up after _____ at night" (20)
92 Attention-getter, or a much-protested aircraft
93 W was always this, when invited to join H on a case
95 Cockney's tête
98 "C'est Si _____"
101 What H considered 53 Across: 4 wds.
108 Towel word
109 Arch., for instance
110 "We turned down a narrow lane . . . which opened into a _____ of the great hospital" (17)
111 Iago's lady
112 Quantity: Abbr.
113 Surgeon's remuneration
114 Adjective or noun endings
115 Made up of two parts

DOWN

1 Make a brief note, with "down"
2 Hebrew measure
3 Actress Caldwell and others
4 De Triomphe and others
5 Japanese admiral
6 Trim; remove
7 " 'You've hit it there, _____,' the young hunter answered" (68)
8 Often the correct form for 96 Down
9 Decorative garb for 46 Down
10 Fond-du-_____, Michigan
11 He didn't get his man — or his stripes
12 Involved with: Sl.
13 Dark yellow paint: Var.
14 "With _____ such men as yourself and Lestrade" (28)
15 Poetic contraction
16 Some; more than two; even one; every
22 How a murder scene should be left: 2 wds.
23 Cockney's shoe parts
27 Spring changeover: Abbr.
28 Mimicked
29 Austrian town, "bei Wien"
30 Drebber and friend's penultimate stop on their European tour (76)
32 He killed John Ferrier (30)
33 Electrically charged atom
34 While on a case, H scarcely thought to do this
35 " 'Let us have some fresh blood,' he said, digging a long _____ into his finger" (18)
36 Since W was always 93 Across, he was never this
37 The Avenging Angels: 2 wds. (63)
39 Like the fine-grained gypsum in vases and statues: Var.

40 "The Science of ____" (23)
45 Nabokov novel
46 The island dance
47 Use up; pay out
50 A stutterer's retort?
52 Constellation's main star
55 "A woman is only a woman, my son, but a good cigar is a ____"
59 "On the Great ____ Plain" (52)
60 "His very person and appearance were such as to strike the attention of the most ____ observer" (20)
62 Fencing sword
64 ". . . I naturally began to run my ____ through it" (23)
66 "Oh wad some power the giftie ____ us": Burns
69 Before, poetically
71 Mlles, in Madrid
75 "Fathers and ____": Turgenev
77 Ring decision: Abbr.
78 When Lucy was forced to do this she pined away and died

82 Boone or O'Brien
85 Prophet; visionary
86 Medieval slave to the soil
90 ____ hope; chance for success: 2 wds.
91 Describing the Ferrier farm during the 29-day countdown
94 Taunt; sneer
95 "____ go Bragh!"
96 "Say, it's awful dry, ____ it?" (53)
97 None were on the streets the night 11 Down found the body (35)
98 French director Roger ____
99 Pot; kettle: Span.
100 Black: Fr.
101 Ejaculation of discovery
102 "____, vigor and vitality"
103 Superlative suffix
104 Sheep
105 The month before our tale begins: Abbr.
106 ____ Koussi: volcano in Chad
107 Swann's ____: Proust

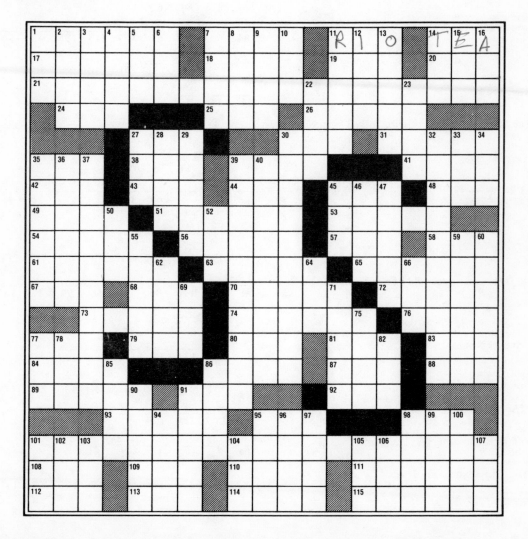

2. The Master speaks, while Watson embarks on his lifelong voyage to amazement, in our first Double-Crostic.

Clues

A The Master. . . . .
$\overline{105}\ \overline{141}\ \overline{83}\ \overline{29}\ \overline{3}\ \overline{57}$

B "_____ can't the English teach their children":
2 wds. . . . .
$\overline{171}\ \overline{150}\ \overline{111}\ \overline{109}\ \overline{199}$

C Agricultural sights during Mormons' first summer:
2 wds. (58).
$\overline{178}\ \overline{27}\ \overline{75}\ \overline{88}\ \overline{127}\ \overline{60}\ \overline{68}\ \overline{106}\ \overline{94}$

$\overline{19}\ \overline{8}$

D "It was upon the 4th _____," our tale's first day:
2 wds. (22).
$\overline{112}\ \overline{95}\ \overline{41}\ \overline{175}\ \overline{101}\ \overline{149}\ \overline{2}$

E "Her attack and her bowing are splendid": Full
Name (36) . . . .
$\overline{152}\ \overline{20}\ \overline{113}\ \overline{49}\ \overline{42}\ \overline{172}\ \overline{180}\ \overline{61}\ \overline{125}$

$\overline{31}\ \overline{16}\ \overline{161}$

F Cleveland's lake.
$\overline{114}\ \overline{31}\ \overline{84}\ \overline{62}$

G Hope's ailment: 2 wds. (77). . . . .
$\overline{184}\ \overline{50}\ \overline{169}\ \overline{63}\ \overline{107}\ \overline{115}\ \overline{198}\ \overline{43}\ \overline{96}$

$\overline{123}\ \overline{162}\ \overline{151}\ \overline{70}\ \overline{140}$

H. Rep. . . . .
$\overline{51}\ \overline{33}\ \overline{76}$

I The Mormons' Board of Directors: 3 wds. (64) . . .
$\overline{1}\ \overline{102}\ \overline{52}\ \overline{44}\ \overline{116}\ \overline{156}\ \overline{196}\ \overline{85}\ \overline{128}$

$\overline{208}\ \overline{34}$

J "Music _____ to soothe the savage breast": 2 wds. . .
$\overline{164}\ \overline{117}\ \overline{53}\ \overline{64}\ \overline{158}\ \overline{194}\ \overline{7}\ \overline{18}\ \overline{79}$

$\overline{135}$

K What H often had to do . . . .
$\overline{25}\ \overline{65}\ \overline{119}\ \overline{139}\ \overline{35}\ \overline{13}\ \overline{131}\ \overline{173}\ \overline{45}$

L De Jure _____, queer old book: 2 wds. (38) . . . . .
$\overline{71}\ \overline{188}\ \overline{146}\ \overline{86}\ \overline{15}\ \overline{66}\ \overline{97}\ \overline{12}\ \overline{163}$

$\overline{120}\ \overline{202}$

M Letter G is one . . . .
$\overline{89}\ \overline{103}\ \overline{121}\ \overline{80}\ \overline{136}\ \overline{201}\ \overline{129}$

N Beatles' song. . . . .
$\overline{157}\ \overline{165}\ \overline{90}\ \overline{26}\ \overline{143}\ \overline{4}\ \overline{130}\ \overline{200}\ \overline{174}$

O "The March _____": 2 wds. . . . .
$\overline{187}\ \overline{176}\ \overline{138}\ \overline{159}\ \overline{91}\ \overline{126}\ \overline{104}$

P Vampires and others . . . .
$\overline{191}\ \overline{72}\ \overline{144}\ \overline{17}\ \overline{92}\ \overline{181}$

Q "_____ fires burning": 3 wds. . . . .
$\overline{142}\ \overline{167}\ \overline{170}\ \overline{154}\ \overline{73}\ \overline{54}\ \overline{195}\ \overline{67}\ \overline{132}$

$\overline{197}\ \overline{5}$

R "Yes, if you have ＿＿ to do": H's invitation, 2 wds. (27)..........................

$\overline{21}$ $\overline{133}$ $\overline{98}$ $\overline{74}$ $\overline{179}$ $\overline{24}$ $\overline{108}$ $\overline{190}$ $\overline{11}$

$\overline{193}$ $\overline{205}$ $\overline{177}$ $\overline{36}$

S Watering spot.........................

$\overline{155}$ $\overline{55}$ $\overline{139}$ $\overline{203}$ $\overline{166}$

T Bereft wife's grief?: 2 wds................

$\overline{37}$ $\overline{182}$ $\overline{32}$ $\overline{153}$ $\overline{46}$ $\overline{204}$ $\overline{68}$ $\overline{207}$ $\overline{10}$

U Charpentier's street: 2 wds. (43)............

$\overline{134}$ $\overline{81}$ $\overline{77}$ $\overline{122}$ $\overline{14}$ $\overline{38}$ $\overline{206}$ $\overline{110}$ $\overline{28}$

$\overline{118}$ $\overline{147}$ $\overline{47}$ $\overline{183}$ $\overline{22}$

V Yorkshire town.........................

$\overline{6}$ $\overline{69}$ $\overline{93}$ $\overline{78}$ $\overline{82}$ $\overline{145}$ $\overline{59}$

W "You have been in ＿＿, I perceive" (19)......

$\overline{23}$ $\overline{99}$ $\overline{160}$ $\overline{87}$ $\overline{124}$ $\overline{56}$ $\overline{148}$ $\overline{39}$ $\overline{185}$

$\overline{168}$ $\overline{137}$

X Mr. Gregson (26)......................

$\overline{192}$ $\overline{100}$ $\overline{9}$ $\overline{186}$ $\overline{40}$ $\overline{48}$

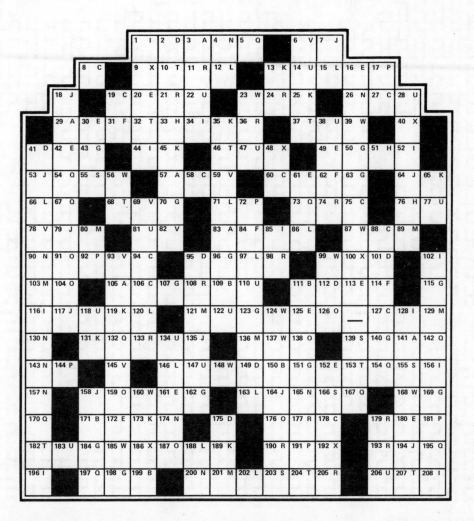

3. Mr. White's Monogram-Maze takes us on one of the epic odysseys of
literature: Watson's peregrinations from a medical degree at the
University of London through his wounding, convalescence and two
vital meetings, then on to the rooms at Baker Street. Find his way
from the one to the other and enjoy the romantic locales—all of
which you will pass through on your way.

FINISH HERE
221B BAKER STREET

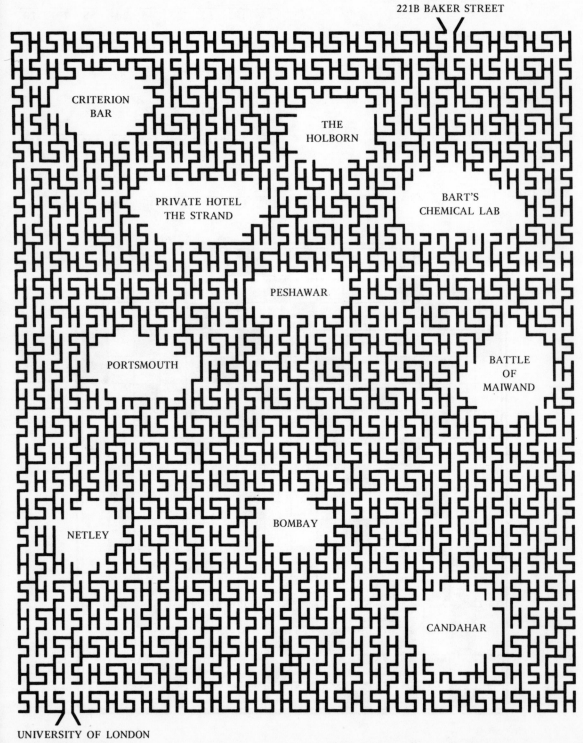

CRITERION
BAR

THE
HOLBORN

PRIVATE HOTEL
THE STRAND

BART'S
CHEMICAL LAB

PESHAWAR

PORTSMOUTH

BATTLE
OF
MAIWAND

BOMBAY

NETLEY

CANDAHAR

UNIVERSITY OF LONDON
START HERE

The Sign of Four

4. Our first Quotation is one of the great aphorisms of the Canon. Its "author" is credited, after the colon.

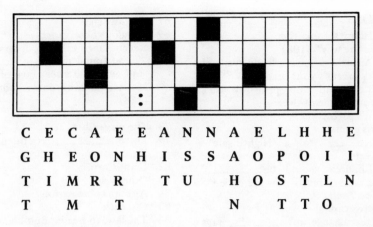

```
C   E   C   A   E   E   A   N   N   A   E   L   H   H   E
G   H   E   O   N   H   I   S   S   A   O   P   O   I   I
T   I   M   R   R       T   U       H   O   S   T   L   N
T       M       T                   N       T   T   O
```

5. This monolith of male chauvinism was certainly vindicated in our next tale, as well as a time or two thereafter.

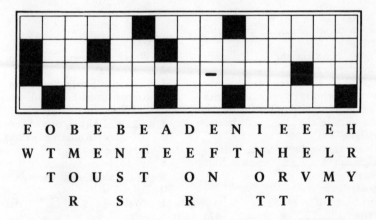

```
E   O   B   E   B   E   A   D   E   N   I   E   E   H
W   T   M   E   N   T   E   E   F   T   N   H   E   L   R
    T   O   U   S   T       O   N       O   R   V   M   Y
    R       S       R           T       T       T
```

6. A Holmesian commandment. The five lines (instead of four) provide an extra challenge.

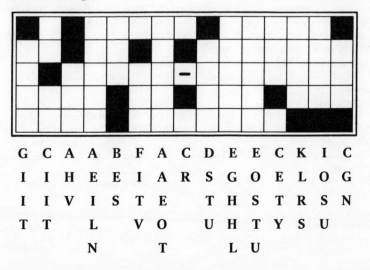

```
G   C   A   A   B   F   A   C   D   E   E   C   K   I   C
I   I   H   E   E   I   A   R   S   G   O   E   L   O   G
I   I   V   I   S   T   E       T   H   S   T   R   S   N
T   T       L       V   O       U   H   T   Y   S   U
            N               T           L   U
```

7. In which the Canon gets its second opportunity to chronicle the vicious ingratitude of Britain's faltering empire.

ACROSS

1 "Holmes took the _____ and led the way" (108)
5 "A little _____'ll do ya," if Brylcreem's your brand
8 The Island imp probably isn't wearing one of these
12 To's partner
15 Iris genus
16 "_____ to a Nightingale": Keats
17 "Children should be _____"
18 "_____ revels now are ended": *The Tempest*
19 Swiss capital
20 "... change my _____ rags into glad rags"
21 "I ... plunged furiously into the latest _____ upon pathology" (97)
23 "It was ... Tonga, who shot one of his cursed _____ into him" (140)
25 "What news on the _____?": *The Merchant of Venice*
26 Attend; take care of: 2 wds.
28 Ivan, Nicholas and Alexander
30 "Be at the third pillar from the left outside the _____ Theatre tonight" (95)
32 Treat snobbishly: Var., Comp.
34 Abdullah _____, one of four (98)
38 Actors' org.
39 The bird-stuffer (115)
41 "The _____ of Four" (87)
42 1501, to Antony
43 Two thousand pounds of solid water: 3 wds.
45 He wrote "The Conqueror Worm"
46 Marcus Welby, for one: Abbr.
47 Theatre executive: Abbr.
48 "Nature had given him a pendulous _____" (100)
51 "I Love Me True," perhaps?: 2 wds.
56 The boatman's plaint?
59 Unique individual: S1.
61 The _____ Islands (95)
62 Exist
63 "The _____ treasure" (103)
64 Entertain
65 Throat lozenge (brand name)

67 Window glass
69 Religious observances
70 Recent medical school graduate
73 "... I found myself in _____-land, with the sweet face of Mary Morstan looking down upon me" (128)
75 Mrs. Hudson (93)
78 The way: Chin.
79 Entre _____, confidentially: Fr.
82 Giant Corp.
83 Otherwise
84 Airport abbreviation
85 Old oath
86 The law, to Beadle Bumble
87 Much-debated aircraft: Pl.
88 A little child
89 Spanish Hausfraus: Abbr.

DOWN

1 Where H spent a lot of time
2 Pub order
3 _____ Smith, boatman (123)
4 Roman household god, usually in the plural
5 _____ Akbar, one of four
6 Nabokov heroine and others
7 Four-poster
8 White House initials
9 Of the air: Comb. form
10 Ogle: 2 wds.
11 "Walking _____": elated, 2 wds.
12 Epée's cousin
13 Autumn hue
14 A great little cookie
22 What H often set the Irregulars
24 Disturb; stir
26 "The Grand _____" of bridge
27 Peered at
28 Southeast Asian
29 "Pray step into my little _____" (100)
31 R in?
32 His Royal Overness: Abbr.
33 Sixties TV adventure group: Init.
35 Aware; understand: Sl.
36 "Once upon a time, long long _____"
37 Frisco, from L.A.

THE SIGN OF FOUR

40 Beckett drama
44 Poetess Millay and others
48 Mauna _____
49 Common verbal or gerundial suffix
50 " . . . a seven _____cent solution" (89)
52 Burdensome responsibility
53 Sixties activist org.
54 Noted inventor's initials
55 To cause to become used to something different: Var.
56 "I . . . am like to spend the other half [of my life] digging drains at _____" (140)
57 Oak, for one
58 Tennis divisions

60 Violated
64 "I fancy that this ally breaks fresh ground in the _____ of crime" (111)
66 Il Duce's son-in-law, and family
68 Favorite Van Gogh site
70 Dorsal bones
71 Indigenous dwellers: Abbr.
72 Dynamites
73 Computer input
74 *The _____ to Morocco*: Hope-Crosby film
76 We go off it in autumn: Abbr.
77 "_____, We Have No Bananas"
78 Chinese New Year
80 Actress Merkel
81 Former draft initials

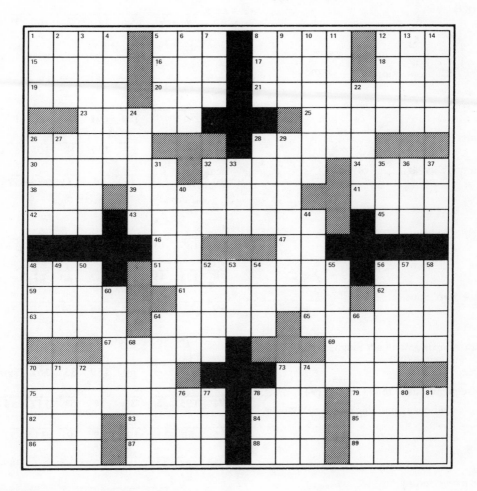

8. In which Holmes indulges his omnipresent ego and his less apparent appreciation of beauty.

Clues

A "The Baker Street ____" (122) . . . .
$\overline{67}$ $\overline{160}$ $\overline{181}$ $\overline{19}$ $\overline{55}$ $\overline{119}$ $\overline{26}$ $\overline{9}$ $\overline{183}$
$\overline{1}$

B "You really are ____"; 2 wds. (96) . . . .
$\overline{42}$ $\overline{68}$ $\overline{141}$ $\overline{149}$ $\overline{10}$ $\overline{27}$ $\overline{50}$ $\overline{177}$ $\overline{107}$
$\overline{133}$ $\overline{153}$

C "I have been guilty of several ____" (91) . . . .
$\overline{82}$ $\overline{11}$ $\overline{134}$ $\overline{111}$ $\overline{69}$ $\overline{184}$ $\overline{28}$ $\overline{36}$ $\overline{75}$
$\overline{51}$

D Spats . . . .
$\overline{29}$ $\overline{37}$ $\overline{102}$ $\overline{144}$ $\overline{174}$

E H took "his ____ syringe from its neat morocco case" (89) . . . .
$\overline{86}$ $\overline{192}$ $\overline{91}$ $\overline{52}$ $\overline{120}$ $\overline{2}$ $\overline{169}$ $\overline{140}$ $\overline{56}$
$\overline{20}$

F ". . . the fifth proposition of ____" (90) . . . .
$\overline{3}$ $\overline{92}$ $\overline{116}$ $\overline{21}$ $\overline{97}$ $\overline{139}$

G "I was consulted last week by François ____" (90).
$\overline{64}$ $\overline{76}$ $\overline{104}$ $\overline{125}$ $\overline{101}$ $\overline{110}$ $\overline{168}$ $\overline{176}$ $\overline{197}$

H Mr. Jones (90) . . . .
$\overline{65}$ $\overline{43}$ $\overline{4}$ $\overline{87}$ $\overline{117}$ $\overline{12}$ $\overline{105}$ $\overline{143}$

I "My mind rebels at ____" (89) . . . .
$\overline{30}$ $\overline{98}$ $\overline{173}$ $\overline{57}$ $\overline{38}$ $\overline{185}$ $\overline{126}$ $\overline{129}$ $\overline{5}$
$\overline{142}$

J "The Hosting of ____": Yeats, 2 wds. . . . .
$\overline{150}$ $\overline{189}$ $\overline{13}$ $\overline{88}$ $\overline{157}$ $\overline{158}$ $\overline{44}$ $\overline{170}$

K "Go on ____"; a binge: 2 wds. . . . .
$\overline{58}$ $\overline{121}$ $\overline{45}$ $\overline{112}$ $\overline{187}$ $\overline{180}$ $\overline{77}$

L "Tea for Two" musical: 3 wds. . . . .
$\overline{59}$ $\overline{22}$ $\overline{172}$ $\overline{70}$ $\overline{186}$ $\overline{122}$ $\overline{130}$ $\overline{78}$ $\overline{175}$
$\overline{188}$ $\overline{163}$

M "Jonathan Small, Mahomet Singh, Abdullah Khan, ____": Full name (98) . . . .
$\overline{79}$ $\overline{83}$ $\overline{93}$ $\overline{60}$ $\overline{159}$ $\overline{33}$ $\overline{162}$ $\overline{190}$ $\overline{46}$

N Term frequently used to describe H (94) . . . .
$\overline{94}$ $\overline{195}$ $\overline{6}$ $\overline{39}$ $\overline{14}$ $\overline{61}$ $\overline{147}$ $\overline{34}$

O ". . . a man who was smoking an ____": 2 wds. (91) . . . .
$\overline{15}$ $\overline{71}$ $\overline{113}$ $\overline{198}$ $\overline{35}$ $\overline{191}$ $\overline{31}$ $\overline{23}$ $\overline{178}$
$\overline{124}$ $\overline{135}$ $\overline{108}$

P Classic movie acronym . . . .
$\overline{136}$ $\overline{73}$ $\overline{7}$ $\overline{165}$

Q Cooper/Kelly masterpiece . . . .
$\overline{128}$ $\overline{32}$ $\overline{179}$ $\overline{8}$ $\overline{123}$ $\overline{72}$ $\overline{103}$ $\overline{155}$

R Immediately afterward: Arch. . . . . $\overline{95}$ $\overline{40}$ $\overline{16}$ $\overline{99}$ $\overline{114}$ $\overline{118}$ $\overline{196}$

S Doyle patterned him after Oscar Wilde . . . . $\overline{96}$ $\overline{166}$ $\overline{171}$ $\overline{146}$ $\overline{17}$ $\overline{137}$

T Punters?: 2 wds. $\overline{74}$ $\overline{138}$ $\overline{41}$ $\overline{53}$ $\overline{100}$ $\overline{115}$

U The air "was heavy with the smell of ____" (122) . $\overline{62}$ $\overline{80}$ $\overline{54}$ $\overline{154}$ $\overline{127}$ $\overline{167}$ $\overline{164}$ $\overline{109}$

V "The Sign ____": 2 wds. . . . . $\overline{151}$ $\overline{47}$ $\overline{63}$ $\overline{193}$ $\overline{89}$ $\overline{106}$

W Awaiting sustenance. $\overline{194}$ $\overline{90}$ $\overline{84}$ $\overline{161}$ $\overline{24}$

X Confederate adversary: 2 wds. . . . . $\overline{48}$ $\overline{131}$ $\overline{148}$ $\overline{156}$ $\overline{18}$ $\overline{25}$ $\overline{145}$ $\overline{182}$

Y Belonging to Shakespeare's Athenian. . . . . $\overline{85}$ $\overline{81}$ $\overline{66}$ $\overline{49}$ $\overline{152}$ $\overline{132}$

1 A	2 E	3 F		4 H	5 I	6 N		7 P	8 Q	9 A	10 B
	11 C	12 H	13 J		14 N	15 O	16 R	17 S	18 X	19 A		20 E	21 F	22 L	23 O
24 W		25 X	26 A	27 B	28 C	29 D	30 I		31 O	32 Q	33 M	34 N		35 O
36 C	37 D	38 I	39 N		40 R	41 T	42 B	43 H	44 J	45 K	46 M		47 V	48 X	49 Y
50 B		51 C	52 E	53 T	54 U		55 A	56 E	57 I	58 K	59 L	60 M	61 N	62 U
63 V	64 G	65 H	66 Y	67 A	68 B	69 C	70 L		71 O	72 Q	73 P		74 T	75 C	76 G
	77 K	78 L	79 M		80 U	81 Y	82 C		83 M	84 W		85 Y	86 E	87 H
88 J	89 V	90 W		91 E	92 F	93 M	94 N	95 R	96 S		97 F	98 I	99 R	100 T	101 C
102 D		103 Q	104 G	105 H	106 V		107 B	108 O	109 U		110 G	111 C	112 K	113 O	114 R
115 T		116 F	117 H	118 R	119 A	120 E		121 K	122 L	123 Q	124 O		125 G	126 I
127 U	128 Q	129 I	130 L	131 X	132 Y		133 B	134 C		135 O		136 P	137 S	138 T	139 F
	140 E	141 B	142 I	143 H		144 D	145 X	146 S	147 N		148 X	149 B	150 J		151 V
152 Y		153 B	154 U	155 Q	156 X		157 J		158 J	159 M	160 A	161 W		162 M	163 L
164 U		165 P	166 S	167 U		168 G	169 E	170 J		171 S	172 L		173 I		174 D
175 L	176 G	177 B	178 O	179 Q	180 K	181 A		182 X	183 A	184 C	185 I	186 L	187 K		188 L
	189 J	190 M	191 O		192 E	193 V	194 W		195 N	196 R	197 G		198 O

A Scandal in Bohemia

9. Here's Mr. White's "Word Detection Puzzle" for one of the best stories in the Canon. Find and circle the words listed below, then put the remaining letters in the "Mystery Quotation" spaces, reading them off from left to right, top to bottom on the grid.

A Scandal in Bohemia

Bell Pull
Betrothal
Bride
Briony Lodge
Brougham

Cabman
Church of St. Monica
Clergyman
Client
Cocaine
Contralto
Costume
Count Von Kramm
Crime

Disguises

Fire

Godfrey Norton

House of Ormstein

Irene Adler

King

Landau
Lawyer
Letter

Marriage
Mews

New Jersey

Photograph
Pipe
Primadonna

Smoke Rocket
Sovereign
Spinster

Word

```
A N N O D A M I R P I P E D I R B
T S I O M A R R I A G E B R S B R
H P C R I M E W S F U G E Y D E I
E I O A E R A L I A N Y L E I T O
S N N L N N O R D I W C L S S R N
O S T E I D E N K A K H P R G O Y
V T R T A O A A L N L M U E U T L
E E A T C L E L D S O S L J I H O
R R L E O T N E I L C V L W S A D
E H T R C A B M A N E E T E E L G
I I O M A H G U O R B R S N S A E
G O D F R E Y N O R T O N L O W A
N Y S T H P A R G O T O H P H U E
W H O U S E O F O R M S T E I N C
O M E M U T S O C L E R G Y M A N
S M O K E R O C K E T D R O W I A
N C H U R C H O F S T M O N I C A
```

Mystery Quotation: "＿ ＿   ＿ ＿ ＿ ＿ ＿ ＿ ＿ ＿

＿ ＿ ＿ ＿ ＿ ＿   ＿ ＿ ＿   ＿ ＿   ＿ ＿ ＿ ＿ ＿ ＿

＿ ＿ ＿   ＿ ＿ ＿ ＿ ＿ ＿ ．"

10. Our Quotation here is one of the earlier examples of Watson's wit, and the Clue Line ranks with Holmes's "Yes, if you have nothing better to do," as one of the truly suave entrances into high adventure.

Clues

A Dandy do-or-die'er: 2 wds. . . . .
$\overline{111}$ $\overline{1}$ $\overline{80}$ $\overline{132}$ $\overline{30}$ $\overline{47}$ $\overline{52}$ $\overline{12}$ $\overline{91}$
$\overline{66}$ $\overline{188}$ $\overline{108}$

B Unusually upset, in error or insane: Sl., 3 wds. . .
$\overline{38}$ $\overline{40}$ $\overline{83}$ $\overline{143}$ $\overline{67}$ $\overline{175}$ $\overline{13}$ $\overline{112}$ $\overline{90}$
$\overline{147}$

C Final outcome or point. . . . .
$\overline{124}$ $\overline{77}$ $\overline{20}$ $\overline{87}$ $\overline{53}$ $\overline{185}$

D A single-masted ship. . . . .
$\overline{127}$ $\overline{94}$ $\overline{68}$ $\overline{113}$

E French operetta composer. . . . .
$\overline{95}$ $\overline{41}$ $\overline{187}$ $\overline{88}$ $\overline{2}$ $\overline{104}$ $\overline{14}$ $\overline{21}$ $\overline{122}$

F Alaskan city. . . . .
$\overline{109}$ $\overline{82}$ $\overline{84}$ $\overline{153}$

G "_____ Town": celebrated one, 4 wds. . . . .
$\overline{128}$ $\overline{144}$ $\overline{42}$ $\overline{165}$ $\overline{55}$ $\overline{22}$ $\overline{154}$ $\overline{173}$ $\overline{114}$
$\overline{157}$ $\overline{190}$ $\overline{179}$ $\overline{105}$

H Hudson's stand-in: 2 wds. (170). . . . .
$\overline{61}$ $\overline{102}$ $\overline{81}$ $\overline{76}$ $\overline{164}$ $\overline{89}$ $\overline{23}$ $\overline{123}$ $\overline{136}$

I International Friends of Holmes: abbr. . . . .
$\overline{62}$ $\overline{56}$ $\overline{172}$ $\overline{174}$

J Godard et al.: 2 wds. . . . .
$\overline{152}$ $\overline{145}$ $\overline{69}$ $\overline{158}$ $\overline{31}$ $\overline{169}$ $\overline{103}$

K Stopped up . . . .
$\overline{24}$ $\overline{39}$ $\overline{97}$ $\overline{115}$ $\overline{148}$ $\overline{178}$

L H "loathed every form of society with his whole _____ soul" (161). . . . .
$\overline{57}$ $\overline{139}$ $\overline{167}$ $\overline{98}$ $\overline{130}$ $\overline{120}$ $\overline{25}$ $\overline{162}$

M Japanese film, remade as *The Outrage* in U.S. . . .
$\overline{85}$ $\overline{106}$ $\overline{125}$ $\overline{5}$ $\overline{58}$ $\overline{54}$ $\overline{129}$ $\overline{171}$

N "_____ east and west . . .": 2 wds. . . . .
$\overline{133}$ $\overline{63}$ $\overline{86}$ $\overline{4}$ $\overline{180}$ $\overline{99}$

O Calls attention; refers or alludes to . . . .
$\overline{116}$ $\overline{3}$ $\overline{149}$ $\overline{150}$ $\overline{137}$ $\overline{32}$ $\overline{75}$

P "You may address me as the Count Von _____" (164) . . . .
$\overline{48}$ $\overline{142}$ $\overline{6}$ $\overline{134}$ $\overline{181}$

Q *The* woman (161) . . . .
$\overline{49}$ $\overline{151}$ $\overline{33}$ $\overline{117}$ $\overline{126}$ $\overline{64}$ $\overline{182}$ $\overline{78}$ $\overline{135}$
$\overline{177}$

R PT-109, for instance: 2 wds. . . . .
$\overline{34}$ $\overline{79}$ $\overline{140}$ $\overline{138}$ $\overline{110}$ $\overline{183}$ $\overline{131}$ $\overline{7}$

S That curious item that accompanies cigars and spirits (162) . . . .

<u>15</u> <u>168</u> <u>118</u> <u>159</u> <u>51</u> <u>35</u> <u>65</u> <u>141</u>

T "The singular tragedy of the Atkinson brothers at ____" (161) . . . .

<u>70</u> <u>16</u> <u>166</u> <u>50</u> <u>43</u> <u>156</u> <u>160</u> <u>176</u>

<u>26</u> <u>170</u> <u>191</u>

U ____Was Won: Epic horse opera, 3 wds. . . . . . .

<u>71</u> <u>186</u> <u>8</u> <u>27</u> <u>59</u> <u>17</u> <u>100</u> <u>161</u> <u>155</u>

<u>44</u>

V The receding ocean: 2 wds. . . . .

<u>60</u> <u>73</u> <u>163</u> <u>45</u> <u>184</u> <u>36</u> <u>72</u>

W Gate fastener . . . .

<u>96</u> <u>9</u> <u>107</u> <u>92</u> <u>28</u>

X Charges; fronts . . . .

<u>18</u> <u>37</u> <u>121</u> <u>189</u> <u>146</u> <u>93</u> <u>10</u>

Y If . . . .

<u>119</u> <u>11</u> <u>74</u> <u>19</u> <u>46</u> <u>101</u> <u>29</u>

Grid:

1 A	2 E	3 O	■	4 N	5 M	6 P	7 R	■	8 U	9 W	10 X	■	11 Y	12 A	13 B
■	14 E	■	15 S	16 T	17 U	18 X	19 Y	■	20 C	21 E	22 G	23 H	24 K	25 L	26 T
■	27 U	28 W	29 Y	30 A	31 J	32 O	33 Q	34 R	35 S	36 V	■	37 X	38 B	■	39 K
40 B	41 E	42 G	43 T	44 U	■	45 V	46 Y	47 A	■	48 P	49 Q	50 T	51 S	52 A	53 C
54 M	■	55 G	56 I	■	57 L	58 M	59 U	60 V	61 H	62 I	63 N	■	64 Q	65 S	66 A
■	67 B	68 D	69 J	■	70 T	71 U	72 V	■	73 V	74 Y	75 O	76 H	■	77 C	78 Q
79 R	80 A	81 H	■	82 F	83 B	■	84 F	85 M	■	86 N	87 C	88 E	89 H	90 B	91 A
92 W	93 X	■	94 D	95 E	96 W	97 K	98 L	99 N	■	100 U	101 Y	102 H	103 J	■	104 E
105 G	106 M	107 W	108 A	109 F	■	110 R	111 A	■	112 B	■	113 D	114 G	115 K	116 O	117 Q
118 S	■	119 Y	120 L	121 X	■	122 E	123 H	■	124 C	125 M	126 Q	127 D	■	128 G	129 M
■	130 L	131 R	132 A	133 N	■	134 P	135 Q	136 H	137 O	138 D	■	139 L	140 R	141 S	142 P
■	143 B	144 G	145 J	■	146 X	147 B	148 K	149 O	150 O	151 Q	152 J	153 F	154 G	155 U	
156 T	157 G	■	158 J	159 S	160 T	161 U	162 L	■	163 V	164 H	165 G	■	166 T	■	167 L
168 S	169 J	170 T	■	171 M	172 I	173 G	■	174 I	175 B	176 T	177 Q	178 K	■	179 G	180 N
181 P	■	182 Q	183 R	■	184 V	185 C	■	186 U	187 E	■	188 A	189 X	190 G	191 T	

The Red-Headed League

11. Here's my Word Detection Puzzle which you may use to bone up on our story for the next puzzle. There are 78 entries, and the remaining letters spell out the Mystery Quotation.

Abbots
Acute
Advertisement
Aldersgate
Archie
Assistant
Attica

Britannica
Budge
Bullion

Candid
Card
Coin
Court

Deal
Derbies
Does
Dog
Duncan Ross

Encyclopaedia
Ennui
Ezekiah Hopkins

Family
Flaubert
Foolscap

Greatcoat
Great Scott

Hair
Hoax

Ideas

Jabez
John Clay
John H. Watson, M.D.

Kensington

Labyrinth
Laugh
Lebanon
Led (Vertical entry only)

Lemon
Lobster
Lure

Merryweather
Morris
Mortimer's

Narrative
Noble

Obese
Once
Orange
Ornament

Pal
Pawnbroker
Pennsylvania
Penny
Photography
Poky

Rest
Roar
Royal
Rubber

Sarasate
Saxe-Coburg Square
Scotland Yard
Settee
Smartest
Stay-at-home
Stout

Ten to two
The Red-Headed League
Three pipe problem
Tobacconist

Unique

Vacancy
Vincent Spaulding
Volume

Wax
Wigs
William

```
D R A Y D N A L T O C S S R E M I T R O M
T L E D H E G D U B A T A O U D O E S O E
A N R T I M E M O E N O M R E B M E R E R
O A E H S R E N T S D B R A A O B R X O R
C W C M B B O L S E I B S A H S I E A A Y
T R T I E M O O B I D A C T N S A R R L W
A N E O E S R L U O I E A L A G O T I S E
E S A L T N I N E N R Y A X W Y E M E U A
R N B T A N N T A B A P E T A I A H G T T
G O C C S E E V R T A C E L N F L A A O H
N R N Y U I L T S E O N U P O E E L B I E
I U E Q C Y S F R B V R O O I L M A I Z R
D I I A S L L S U E E D L N D P C A E A D
L N N N T A O R A K B S A E L C E K N E M
U A N P U S G P E O C R D E O U I E A R N
A E B B H S C N A A J A I N B A D L R R O
P L E Y Q O S O P E E A I T H U E S E H S
S R D U R I T V T H D S B H A V L K G M T
T E A E N I G O D T T I O E I N O L A I A
N R T G R E N E G R E P A T Z R N R I T W
E T T T M S R T C R K H A C B E T I T O H
C O R U E E G C H I A R G N U E E I C O N
N S L U H E O A N T R P W U S T C C A A H
I O T T O I O S T A U A H T A A E X N T O
V A C A N C Y N N E P O K Y A L C N H O J
```

Mystery Quotation: "__ ' __ __ __ __ __ __ ' __ __ __ __ __ __ __ __ __ - __ __ , __ __ __ __ __ __ __ , __ __ __ __ __ __ __ __ ."

12. The Starting Box for this Diagramless, as for future ones, may be found on the last answer page.

ACROSS

1 "He has a white splash of _____ upon his forehead" (183)
5 "Whose _____ are you on, anyway?!"
6 "... he sat in the _____ wrapped in the most perfect happiness" (185)
9 "... an aimless smile that hovers in the _____": Eliot
11 "Have you the chisel and the _____?" (189)
15 "At first it was but a _____ spark upon the stone pavement" (188)
17 "Once _____ a time"
18 "Duncan Ross" made sure Jabez wasn't wearing one (180)
19 You can find it in an atlas
21 "_____ hundred flowers blossom": Maoist adage, 2 wds.
22 Trail
23 "He is as brave as a _____" (187)
25 Wet, driving snow
28 Mario _____, linguist
29 "... he was running a _____ to some other building" (190)
31 "_____ and Don'ts"
33 Dry: Fr.
36 Jackie O's late magnate
37 Actual
40 Poker wager
42 Recent, latest or new: Pref.
43 Hair color, of some significance to this tale
44 Soldier's retreat: Abbr.
45 "... a drab waistcoat with a heavy brassy _____ chain" (177)
47 Rooming house: Sl.
49 Something H never does
50 "... the League has a _____" (179)
54 Spaulding
56 "... and he himself has been to _____ and Oxford" (186)
57 British beverage, customarily
59 Possessive pronoun
60 Durrell novel
61 "We are _____ in an enemy's country" (184)
63 New York theater award
64 Chemical suffix
65 Duncan (189)
70 Public uproar
71 "_____ ignotum pro magnifico" (177)

DOWN

1 Donkey
2 Op. _____: footnote phrase
3 Gilbert & Sullivan's Princess
4 State: Abbr.
7 "If you can do nothing better than _____ at me" (182)
8 Title
10 Edge
11 "... the _____ might be removed" (190)
12 Mimicked
13 "_____ the dogs": degenerate, 2 wds.
14 Unexpected difficulty
15 "I _____ a cigarette on a parking meter": Dylan
16 Touch lightly and quickly
18 "There is _____ in your eyes" (180)
20 Young canine
22 One of the items Jabez had to provide (181)
24 "_____ and the Swan": Yeats
25 Betelgeuse, for one
26 "The £4 a week was a _____ which must draw him" (189)
27 Feminine name
30 Romanian coin
32 Depot: Abbr.
33 "I raised my snicker _____": The Mikado
34 Poetic contractions
35 Bunks
38 "... those who were unacquainted with his methods would look _____ at him" (185)
39 Beef or pork cut
41 English composer, 1857-1934
46 Purchase
48 Percent: Abbr.
50 Presidential prerogative
51 "Rub-a-dub-dub, three men in _____": 2 wds.
52 Rabbit: Var.

53 Affirmative response
54 "Vincent Spaulding did what he could to _____ me up" (181)
55 French article: Pl.
58 Gorilla

62 Feminine name
66 _____-Magnon Man
67 Pronoun
68 Electrically charged particle
69 French season

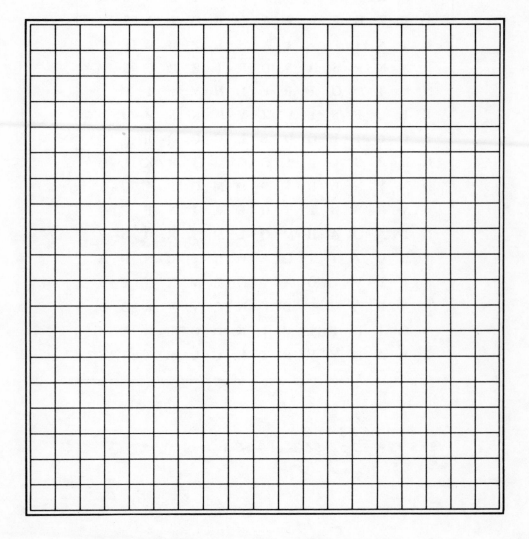

A Case of Identity

13. A Victorian melodrama of passions thwarted and evil laid bare—something Holmes almost did to Windibank's back with a horsewhip. Letter counts for the two Hidden Phrases are below. Hint: Find the longest word and work back and forward from it.

```
N  P  X  V  Y  E  D  T  E  S  F  C  K  B  A
A  N  H  A  F  I  Z  V  R  S  T  O  D  E  K
I  B  T  H  E  R  E  A  L  F  O  I  A  S  U
E  T  K  J  P  W  I  X  S  L  B  H  C  E  T
S  X  N  V  S  A  S  D  R  I  R  R  U  S  M
N  U  T  M  O  T  F  E  L  N  Y  E  I  M  L
E  E  U  F  S  L  V  Z  Y  H  K  S  P  D  M
S  C  C  I  E  O  D  E  E  G  O  Q  L  J  S
H  H  P  S  E  S  I  O  G  E  J  R  K  L  U
D  N  Y  N  W  R  F  O  D  M  O  P  A  Q  S
E  M  R  P  H  E  T  H  E  W  T  X  F  C  G
N  P  A  O  A  H  M  Q  L  M  T  R  O  B  E
I  X  U  Z  T  T  C  E  W  U  T  U  N  D  A
A  F  L  V  E  O  A  Y  O  E  M  H  W  E  N
R  S  P  A  H  R  E  P  N  C  V  V  R  O  D
T  G  I  H  E  I  M  I  K  D  O  E  W  A  X
E  V  A  H  Y  V  B  Z  H  C  U  M  S  J  S
```

1. 7-1-4-7-6-2-3-4-6-8
2. 5-2-2-4-5-2-5-2-2-6-3-2-4-9-2-3-5

The Boscombe Valley Mystery

14. From "The Land Down Under" springs this tale of old wrongs and family pride. Work this first Semi-Crostic to discover another Holmesian maxim. Reminder: The boldface numbers in the 'Words' column are used more than once.

Definitions   **Words**

The murderer $\overline{24}$ $\overline{39}$ $\overline{4}$ $\overline{33}$ $\overline{20}$ $\overline{17}$

————— Valley $\overline{35}$ $\overline{9}$ $\overline{40}$ $\overline{21}$ $\overline{34}$ $\overline{15}$ $\overline{35}$ $\overline{27}$

Alice, to John $\overline{19}$ $\overline{30}$ $\overline{39}$ $\overline{14}$ $\overline{11}$ $\overline{44}$ $\overline{22}$ $\overline{4}$

Where W experienced camp life (202) $\overline{30}$ $\overline{41}$ $\overline{14}$ $\overline{29}$ $\overline{32}$ $\overline{13}$ $\overline{6}$ $\overline{7}$ $\overline{1}$ $\overline{42}$ $\overline{31}$

Miss Moran (203) $\overline{23}$ $\overline{32}$ $\overline{28}$ $\overline{12}$ $\overline{5}$ $\overline{8}$ $\overline{43}$ $\overline{27}$

Where the killer got his start (208) $\overline{26}$ $\overline{25}$ $\overline{43}$ $\overline{10}$ $\overline{38}$ $\overline{4}$ $\overline{37}$ $\overline{42}$

W's was slovenly (204) $\overline{40}$ $\overline{2}$ $\overline{30}$ $\overline{36}$ $\overline{18}$

W's wandered (209) $\overline{32}$ $\overline{1}$ $\overline{28}$ $\overline{3}$ $\overline{8}$ $\overline{44}$ $\overline{6}$ $\overline{16}$ $\overline{31}$

Solution:

$\overline{1}$ $\overline{2}$ $\overline{3}$ $\overline{4}$ $\overline{5}$ $\overline{6}$ $\overline{7}$ $\quad$ $\overline{8}$ $\overline{9}$ $\overline{10}$ $\overline{11}$ $\overline{12}$ $\overline{13}$ $\overline{14}$ $\quad$ $\overline{15}$ $\overline{16}$ $\overline{17}$ $\overline{18}$

$\overline{19}$ $\overline{20}$ $\overline{21}$ $\overline{22}$ $\overline{23}$ $\overline{24}$ $\overline{25}$ $\overline{26}$ $\overline{27}$ $\quad$ $\overline{28}$ $\overline{29}$ $\overline{30}$ $\overline{31}$ $\quad$ $\overline{32}$ $\overline{33}$

$\overline{34}$ $\overline{35}$ $\overline{36}$ $\overline{37}$ $\overline{38}$ $\overline{39}$ $\overline{40}$ $\quad$ $\overline{41}$ $\overline{42}$ $\overline{43}$ $\overline{44}$

15. "There, but for the grace of God, goes Sherlock Holmes."

Definitions   **Words**

The murdered man $\overline{45}$ $\overline{18}$ $\overline{23}$ $\overline{9}$ $\overline{33}$ $\overline{28}$ $\overline{19}$ $\overline{3}$

J.T. was a "landed" one (203) $\overline{12}$ $\overline{21}$ $\overline{43}$ $\overline{30}$ $\overline{33}$ $\overline{22}$ $\overline{35}$ $\overline{28}$ $\overline{43}$ $\overline{21}$

          shire (203) $\overline{2}$ $\overline{6}$ $\overline{21}$ $\overline{11}$ $\overline{8}$ $\overline{5}$ $\overline{44}$ $\overline{4}$

The other doctor (208) $\overline{1}$ $\overline{27}$ $\overline{13}$ $\overline{38}$ $\overline{31}$ $\overline{42}$ $\overline{7}$

H and W's A.M course (204) $\overline{26}$ $\overline{11}$ $\overline{16}$ $\overline{10}$ $\overline{42}$ $\overline{14}$ $\overline{44}$ $\overline{4}$

H saw whither this led him (207) $\overline{29}$ $\overline{15}$ $\overline{37}$ $\overline{32}$ $\overline{20}$ $\overline{34}$ $\overline{35}$ $\overline{25}$ $\overline{22}$ $\overline{40}$

Crimes difficult to "bring home" (202) $\overline{8}$ $\overline{35}$ $\overline{9}$ $\overline{10}$ $\overline{17}$ $\overline{21}$ $\overline{11}$ $\overline{36}$ $\overline{39}$ $\overline{41}$ $\overline{46}$

It was gray (213) $\overline{18}$ $\overline{13}$ $\overline{43}$ $\overline{9}$ $\overline{24}$

Solution:

$\overline{1}$ $\overline{2}$ $\overline{3}$ $\overline{4}$ $\overline{5}$ $\overline{6}$ $\overline{7}$ $\quad$ $\overline{8}$ $\overline{9}$ $\overline{10}$ $\overline{11}$ $\quad$ $\overline{12}$ $\overline{13}$ $\overline{14}$ $\overline{15}$

$\overline{16}$ $\overline{17}$ $\overline{18}$ $\overline{19}$ $\quad$ $\overline{20}$ $\overline{21}$ $\overline{22}$ $\overline{23}$ $\quad$ $\overline{24}$ $\overline{25}$ $\quad$ $\overline{26}$ $\overline{27}$ $\overline{28}$ $\overline{29}$ $\quad$ $\overline{30}$ $\overline{31}$ $\overline{32}$ $\overline{33}$

$\overline{34}$ $\overline{35}$ $\overline{36}$ $\overline{37}$ $\overline{38}$ $\overline{39}$ $\overline{40}$ $\overline{41}$ $\quad$ $\overline{42}$ $\overline{43}$ $\overline{44}$ $\overline{45}$ $\overline{46}$

The Five Orange Pips

16. From reading the Canon, one would assume America was overrun with vicious secret societies whose members spent most of their time seeking revenge in distant quarters of the globe. Here's another such tale, this of the dreaded KKK.

ACROSS

1 "... in spite of the _____" (217)
5 Distress initials
8 Competent
9 "... I had begun to hope that this _____ had passed" (222)
12 "The _____ Mendicant Society" (218)
15 Minute particles of matter
16 Ruth or Zaharias
17 Time span
19 _____ Poetica
20 Hogs' home
22 Grounded bird of Australia
23 Fat
25 _____ Housman, poet
26 Scot tot
28 "Again Holmes _____ in the air" (223)
29 R.R. stop
30 "... in the grasp of some resistless, inexorable _____" (223)
33 It's time for this around 5 P.M.
34 "... in the grate there was a mass of black, fluffy _____" (220)
36 Dutch cheese
38 BPOE member
39 Birds' beaks or animals' snouts
40 Lummox
42 Bronze: Lat.
43 Lindy's flight
44 "... a heading which sent a _____ to my heart" (227)
47 _____ — Magnon Man
50 Weakness; failing
52 Parking _____
53 "... it is more likely to be some _____ of the landlady's" (218)
55 "Cry 'Havoc,' and let slip the _____ of war": Julius Caesar
58 You Know Me, _____: Ring Lardner
59 Elias, to John (219)
60 Noted Prince's nickname
61 Deals: Abbr.

63 Eggs: Lat.
64 Sweet potato
66 Nevada hot spot
67 King of Norway, 995-1000
69 "Do not think of _____" (224)
71 Elinor or Post
72 Metal
73 Steamer: Abbr.
74 Coming up

DOWN

1 "... and that is all which we shall ever know of the _____ of the Lone Star" (229)
2 Lincoln or Vigoda
3 "Excellent. We have already a _____" (225)
4 "What could be the reason for his overpowering _____? (220)
5 "... he looked very _____ and puzzled now that the same thing had come upon himself" (222)
6 Baseball events
7 Sellout sign
10 Sergeant majors: Abbr.
11 "... my father entered into possession of the _____" (221)
12 The first murder victim
13 Papa's mate
14 "Well, to come to an end ... and not to _____ your patience" (221)
18 _____, a ball and a glove: 2 wds.
19 In a fog; confused
21 Some votes
24 12 Down's 13 Down
27 Scandinavian name
29 "_____ for J.O." (228)
31 "The _____ reasoner would, when he had once been shown a single fact" (224)

32 "On the inside of the cover was a paper _____" (221)
34 Standoffish
35 Kong's island home
37 Manuscripts. Abbr.
38 Urban railways
41 *Wind in the Willows* character
44 "The man who entered was young, . . . well-groomed and trimly _____" (218)
45 "I have them in the _____ of my hand" (228)
46 "The _____ Girl"
47 Consumer Research of North America: Abbr.
48 Extinct bird
49 Sole

51 ". . . we have our web to weave, while theirs is already _____" (224)
53 "As _____ could correctly describe a whole animal" (225)
54 "_____, year out": 2 wds.
56 "I shall set my hand upon this _____" (228)
57 _____ gin fizz
62 Crafty
63 "Just for the heck _____": 2 wds.
65 Mother: Fr.
66 Lease
68 Belonging to 58 Across
70 _____ *Populi*: Voice of the People

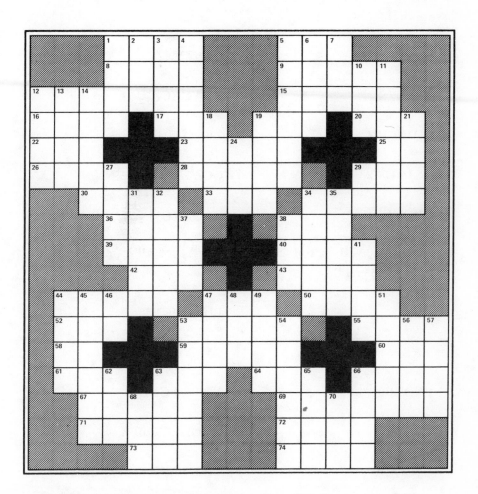

17. Here are three Cryptic-Quizzes, each employing different codes. In this first one, representing people from our story, take special note of the third, fourth and fifth names.

PII	QENSV JVIIFSHC
TELEQSVI	WLIVPSGO LSPQIW
NSLR WAEMR	KVMGI TEXIVWSRW
NSLR AEXWSR	QENSV TVIRHIVKEWX
NSLR STIRWLEA	GSP IPMEW STIRWLEA

18. Places. Holmes's client lived at one of these sites—and died at another.

PAAV	OZIIZNNZZ
NPNNZS	KJIYDXCZMMT
CJMNCVH	ZVNO GJIYJI
AGJMDYV	OCZ XVMJGDIVN
NVQVIIVC	RVOZMGJJ WMDYBZ

19. Things, If A=B in this code, then B=A, for all letters. N.B.: A does *not* equal B.

CVC	FHAQVNY
XRLF	ZNVY-OBNG
PNOYR	YBAR FGNE
EVSYR	NYOREG QBPX
RJGNGR	TERRA-FPHZZRQ CBBY

20. Things are not what they seem in this story of a one-man Amateur Mendicant Society, nor are they in the sentences below. They're Holmes's comments upon Watson's comradeship, but certain words in one belong in the other, and vice versa. The lines below the ordered pairings of words are provided for work space.

| A | trusty | a | grand | gift | of silence | and | it makes |
| You | have | comrade | is | always | of use | Watson | a chronicler |

____ ____ ____ ____ ____ __ ____ __ _____

____ ____ ____ ____ ____ __ ____ __ _____

| you | more | invaluable. |
| still | quite | so. |

_____ _____ _____

_____ _____ _____

21. J = D in this rare example of Holmesian self-effacement.

O IUTLKYY ZNGZ O NGBK HKKT GY HROTJ GY G SURK, HAZ

OZ OY HKZZKX ZU RKGXT COYJUS RGZK ZNGT TKBKX ZU

RKGXT OZ GZ GRR.

22. And an even rarer example of Holmesian self-reproach.

B	E	D	E	I	E	K	E	D	S	C	H	A
I	I	H	E	R	C	R	O	E		F	O	O
M		N	G	S	E	R	T	O		T		R
R			K		C		V	S				

The Adventure of the Blue Carbuncle

23. Christmas at Baker Street, in which "a bird will be the chief feature," and a couple of unseasonably wicked quotations of the Master's, for you to ferret out from the following. Letter counts below.

```
W  H  O  A  G  N  L  F  G  N  S  P  E  T  A
M  W  H  R  G  E  G  A  L  L  O  W  S  P  E
U  O  E  Q  E  F  H  M  O  R  N  A  O  H  B
G  U  J  S  J  E  D  T  O  T  N  L  T  Y  D
I  L  R  S  E  Y  Z  Y  O  D  I  C  P  N  E
J  D  K  I  X  I  E  N  T  C  E  F  Q  E  N
T  I  S  D  E  V  C  H  E  G  D  D  I  O  I
H  E  B  L  R  S  E  N  T  C  W  G  E  P  A
I  M  A  U  N  P  R  O  E  P  B  H  E  E  T
N  T  P  O  F  R  S  K  J  I  L  N  D  T  E
K  Y  U  W  M  I  A  U  A  B  C  O  P  O  R
A  T  O  Y  S  S  Q  R  P  H  A  I  P  N  K
K  T  H  T  L  O  F  E  Z  P  O  C  F  M  A
E  E  T  A  T  N  G  K  U  E  L  V  B  E  I
D  R  V  R  T  W  X  L  T  H  U  Y  U  A  D
C  P  O  S  L  X  M  Y  V  W  T  H  E  I  R
E  K  F  G  A  M  B  O  S  T  A  V  M  L  E
```

1. 3-5-5-4-2-6-1-3-5-2-1-8-2-3-7-3-3-6
2. 1-2-3-8-2-3-6-2-6-5-12

24. Charming Quotations, placed here mainly to avoid beginning a crossword puzzle on a right-hand page, a *faux pas* for which I would have received nasty letters I don't need.

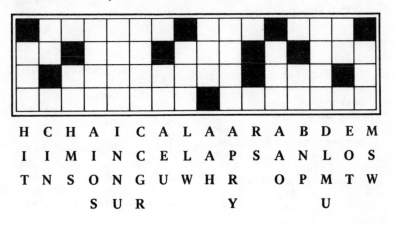

```
H C H A I C A L A A R A B D E M
I I M I N C E L A P S A N L O S
T N S O N G U W H R   O P M T W
    S U R       Y       U
```

25. Ditto.

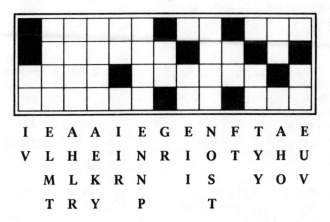

```
  I E A A I E G E N F T A E
  V L H E I N R I O T Y H U
    M L K R N   I S   Y O V
    T R Y   P       T
```

26. Alas, ditto.

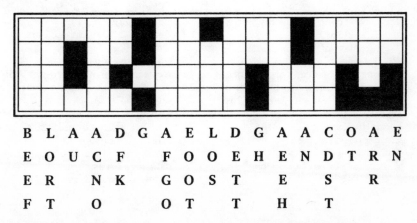

```
B L A A D G A E L D G A A C O A E
E O U C F   F O O E H E N D T R N
E R   N K   G O S T   E   S   R
F T   O     O T   T   H   T
```

The Adventure of the Speckled Band

27. The infamous star of our current tale is one of the most unpleasant villains in all the Canon, and his name is one of the most apt. If you don't know of whom I speak, start putting together 6 Down.

ACROSS

1 "... the _____ survivor of one of the oldest Saxon families" (259)
5 Paid notice: Abbr.
9 Fastening band
14 "... a small dog _____ hung on one corner of the bed" (268)
15 "... we hired a _____ at the station inn" (265)
16 "... it was concerned with an opal _____. (259)
17 Dinner and a show, for instance
18 Parts; divisions: Abbr.
19 Pantsuit, for instance
20 Helen or Julia (259)
23 Wayside hostelry
24 Kitty sound
25 "I can't believe _____ the whole thing": Ad line, 2 wds.
27 Young Holstein
31 Otherwise
34 Where "the speckled band" and others come from (272)
36 Resort lake
37 "... how subtle are the links which bind two _____" (261)
39 Editor's word
40 It startled H and W in the night
41 Refines or extracts (metal)
43 Exist: Span.
44 Chum
45 "... scaffolding had been erected against the _____ wall" (266)
46 Of the air: Comb. form
48 English brew
49 Drs.' org.
52 "The shutters cut off the least _____ of light" (271)
53 "Yippee-ki-_____-yay"
55 "... the control of my own _____" (259)
60 "... a square of Wilton _____" (267)
62 Painting and dance, for instance
64 "... there is someone more cunning than himself upon his _____" (266)
65 Poetized: Var.
66 Clear soups
68 Tom Joad, for one
69 _____ of Eden: Steinbeck
70 "_____ Rider"

71 Over
73 "And now I _____ that you will lay before us everything" (259)
74 "The building was of gray, _____-blotched stone" (266)
76 Julia, to Helen
80 Tome
81 "... old-fashioned shutters with broad _____ bars" (262)
85 "... her _____ seemed to give way and she fell" (262)
86 Apple juice (brand name)
87 Black: Fr.
88 1945 and 1979, for instance
89 "... I hope to get some _____ which may help us" (265)
90 She's "like a dream come true"

DOWN

1 Graduate degree
2 Automobile group: Abbr.
3 Attention-getting sound
4 "... my sister was troubled by _____ of the strong Indian cigars": 2 wds. (261)
5 A golf ball, a driver and _____: 2 wds.
6 The villain of the piece: title and name
7 Vessel: Lat.
8 W.C. necessity
9 Shock
10 Prefix for mouse or willow
11 British fighting unit: Abbr.
12 Jackie's O
13 _____ Nixon
18 "The _____ of Kilimanjaro: Hemingway
19 "_____ Day at a Time: TV series
21 Note in the musical scale
22 Western hemisphere group: Abbr.
23 "_____ a grand night for singing"
26 Fitting
27 "... we shall call a _____ and drive to Waterloo" (265)
28 "Man with _____": poem and painting, 2 wds.
29 Minnesota state bird

30 Resist; parry, usually with "off"
31 Curve
32 Actor Herbert _____
33 "A Boy Named _____": Johnny Cash song
35 Had lunch
36 Natural endowment
38 "The lady . . . _____ in bewilderment" (259)
40 Indonesian island
42 ". . . back in the old family _____" (260)
44 Loudspeaker system: Abbr.
47 Suffix for dentist or jewel
49 Land measure
50 Mother of Hermes
51 "_____ and the man I sing": Vergil
54 Megacorporation: Init.
56 Where H and W stayed in Surrey: 2 wds.
57 Papa, to an acorn
58 1101, to Catullus
59 Scratch (out)

61 ". . . the doctor met his fate . . . playing with a dangerous _____" (272)
62 _____ Poetica
63 "My Little Grass _____": song
66 Sack
67 Green Stamp firm, 'n' for short
70 Poetic contraction
72 _____ cummings
73 "Good Queen _____"
75 "_____ Subscript": Frost poem
76 _____ King: Fifties TV hero
77 Chemical suffix
78 Atlantic or Pacific
79 Jerry _____ Horst, Ford's first press secretary
80 Long feathered neckwear
82 Aussie marsupial, for short
83 ". . . a strong smell of burning _____ and heated metal" (271)
84 FDR-era acronym
86 AMA member

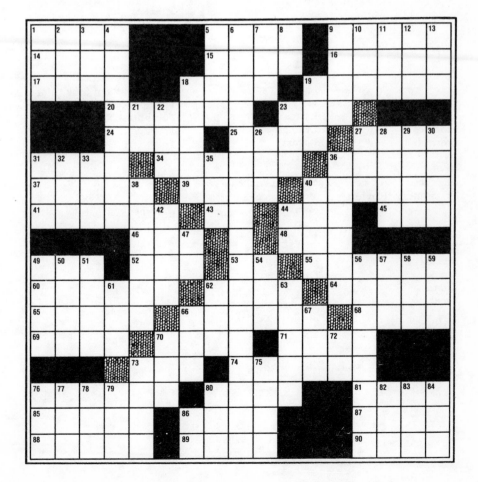

28. Here's a jumbo Word Detection puzzle for those of you who have not yet had enough of Baboons, Devils, Swamp Adders and—Terrible Manifold Wickedness—The Roylotts of Stoke Moran.

Acres
Age
Ajar
Amiable
Amid
Anger
April
Armitage
Arms
Avert

Baboon
Bachelors
Bell
Bell-rope
Bile
Blue

Calcutta
Cane
Carpet
Cases
Client
Cord
Corridor
Crab
Crocuses
Crown Inn

Devil
Dog-cart
Dr. Grimesby Roylott

Easy
Eleven
Eley's No. Two
Erected
Errand
Estate
Event

Family
Farintosh
Feeble

Gate
Glove

Handkerchiefs
Heirs
Honoria
Housekeeper
Hubbub

India
Insist
Iron
Issue

Jack-in-Office
John Watson
Joy
Julia

Lad
Lady
Last
Leatherhead
Lichen
Lips

Manifold Wickedness
Mantelpiece
Marriage
Mass
Metropolis

Only
Opal

Palm
Parapet
Pipe
Plantation

Rat
Real
Ruin

Save
Scent
Shone
Sitting-room
Slope
Staples
Stepdaughter
Stoner
Strain
Swamp Adder

Tassel
Tents
Terrible
The Roylotts of Stoke Moran
The Speckled Band
Toothbrush
Track
Trap

Vague

Wants
Westphail

```
T T O L Y O R Y B S E M I R G R D E T C E R E
H H A N D K E R C H I E F S R O L E H C A B G
E E E L O T H O E V O L G T S I E S V N S L A
R C A S E S R O A T H N N A C U U G G I Y U T
O D E Y P D T G U R H E O H I R E E A R L E I
Y W L I I E U A E S I G E R B R R D A I N E M
L N T D P E C D W L E N U H I O R J I T D E R
O E R O E L D K C N E K T A D A A A S M T N A
T S A L N A E R L L H O E I D C N S M R A F I
T T C T P S O T I E O O R E R P D E O A A N L
S N K M H C Y B N T D R J E P M E P D R S I U
O A A O U E E E A O B S O L E O T I I P L J
F W N S I L R R L C M S A A Y L R N S S E E A
S E E I L D R H S E I A P N I T T T N E C S C
T S E R U I O T E T V L S S D O S N N A S T K
O T O B B R A G T A A A N S S R I L N E R A I
K P A L L S N I C N D K S H I N E E I A V T N
E H E A S E N O T A Y E U E W I T N P R N E O
M A D E L G T A O L R B H O L E B I O A P P F
O I L E R R T N I B B T R L P P G A I T A A F
R L V O E I O M N U A C E R D I A R R L S R I
A E O V O R A A B E L B A I M A T T U C L A C
N M A N I F O L D W I C K E D N E S S L O P E
```

Mystery Quotation: _ _ _ _ _ _ _ _ _ _ _ _

_ _ _ _ _ _ _ _ _ _ _ _

The Adventure of the Engineer's Thumb

29. To commiserate over Holmes's miserable failure in this gruesome tale, here's an easy one. Fill in the words from the list below until the list is empty and the grid is full.

4 LETTERS
Evil

6 LETTERS
Eyford
Strive
Venner
Victor

7 LETTERS
Bandage
Colonel
Dooties
Machine

8 LETTERS
Actually
Chestnut
Matheson
Stamping
Thinness
Victoria

9 LETTERS
Breakfast
Fleshless
Greenwich
Hatherley
Inception
Stimulant

10 LETTERS
Englishman
Operations
Profession
Recompense
Rose-bushes

11 LETTERS
Accommodate
Advertising
Bloodstains

12 LETTERS
Fuller's-earth

13 LETTERS
Eavesdroppers

The Adventure of the Noble Bachelor

30. Words to Live By, from the Stiff Upper Lip Department.

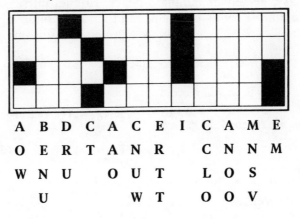

```
A  B  D  C  A  C  E  I  C  A  M  E
O  E  R  T  A  N  R     C  N  N  M
W  N  U     O  U  T     L  O  S
   U        W  T        O  O  V
```

31. One of the Master's better shockers.

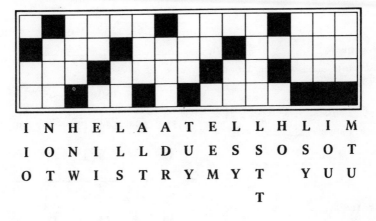

```
I  N  H  E  L  A  A  T  E  L  L  H  L  I  M
I  O  N  I  L  L  D  U  E  S  S  O  S  O  T
O  T  W  I  S  T  R  Y  M  Y  T     Y  U  U
                        T
```

32. What? Not even Peanuts?!

```
E  E  A  A  A  D  E  N  H  C  A  C  D  G  M
H  N  C  E  G  N  N  T  O  E  H  I  N  I  N
I  X  R  E  P  O     W  S  T  O  L  R  M  T
I     L     T  Y           N  U
```

The Adventure of the Beryl Coronet

33. Alexander gets a lesson in familial fidelity, Holmes pursues with delicacy and brilliance a most trying problem, and I am left wondering how anyone, no matter how "exalted," could hock a "public possession of the empire."

Clues

A "It was naturally my _____ that he should succeed me in my business" (304) . . . .

<u>1</u> <u>163</u> <u>115</u> <u>153</u> <u>175</u> <u>164</u> <u>84</u> <u>145</u> <u>183</u>

B ". . . we believe her to be a _____ good girl in every way" (304) . . . .

<u>177</u> <u>16</u> <u>172</u> <u>76</u> <u>116</u> <u>88</u> <u>55</u> <u>62</u> <u>103</u>

<u>37</u>

C Symbolized by a light bulb in cartoons . . . .

<u>108</u> <u>2</u> <u>179</u> <u>17</u>

D Gourmet condiment: 2 wds. . . . .

<u>28</u> <u>187</u> <u>63</u> <u>73</u> <u>109</u> <u>122</u> <u>38</u>

E His love kept him silent: Full name (304). . . . . . .

<u>117</u> <u>39</u> <u>200</u> <u>86</u> <u>134</u> <u>93</u> <u>98</u> <u>3</u> <u>170</u>

<u>69</u> <u>159</u> <u>146</u>

F Presidential prerogatives . . . .

<u>18</u> <u>196</u> <u>85</u> <u>29</u> <u>94</u> <u>79</u>

G ". . . one of the servants' _____ with her wooden-legged lover" (314) . . . .

<u>19</u> <u>30</u> <u>150</u> <u>138</u> <u>64</u> <u>189</u> <u>104</u> <u>99</u>

H Kurosawa film . . . .

<u>180</u> <u>193</u> <u>144</u> <u>130</u> <u>56</u> <u>80</u> <u>151</u> <u>4</u>

I "In life or in death, I am ever _____": 3 wds. (312) . . . .

<u>52</u> <u>5</u> <u>160</u> <u>135</u> <u>118</u> <u>77</u> <u>32</u> <u>40</u> <u>105</u>

<u>139</u> <u>110</u> <u>81</u> <u>147</u> <u>46</u>

J Vaudeville dance: Hyph.. . . . .

<u>53</u> <u>87</u> <u>173</u> <u>6</u> <u>158</u> <u>192</u> <u>106</u> <u>31</u>

K "He was wild, _____, and, to speak the truth, I could not trust him" (304) . . . .

<u>10</u> <u>54</u> <u>123</u> <u>100</u> <u>90</u> <u>190</u> <u>20</u>

L "Sherlock Holmes pushed him down into the _____": Hyph. (302). . . . .

<u>33</u> <u>124</u> <u>171</u> <u>191</u> <u>91</u> <u>165</u> <u>174</u> <u>57</u> <u>199</u>

M Derby site: 2 wds. . . . .

<u>41</u> <u>65</u> <u>154</u> <u>101</u> <u>181</u> <u>195</u> <u>21</u> <u>11</u> <u>82</u>

<u>194</u>

N The number of beryls in the restored coronet: Hyph. (308). . . . .

<u>47</u> <u>12</u> <u>95</u> <u>34</u> <u>89</u> <u>66</u> <u>22</u> <u>128</u> <u>125</u>

<u>140</u>

O "_____ on the totem pole": 2 wds. . . . .

<u>111</u> <u>141</u> <u>48</u> <u>42</u> <u>119</u> <u>58</u> <u>96</u>

P "_____ fixe" . . . .

<u>184</u> <u>126</u> <u>23</u> <u>112</u>

Q Alexander's bank site, _____ Street (302) . . . .
$\overline{24}$ $\overline{167}$ $\overline{102}$ $\overline{35}$ $\overline{13}$ $\overline{127}$ $\overline{120}$ $\overline{143}$ $\overline{166}$

$\overline{202}$ $\overline{156}$ $\overline{185}$

R _____ *Who Came in from the Cold:* 2 wds. . . . . .
$\overline{14}$ $\overline{178}$ $\overline{121}$ $\overline{129}$ $\overline{70}$ $\overline{182}$

S Family sculpture, with snakes . . . .
$\overline{36}$ $\overline{59}$ $\overline{25}$ $\overline{186}$ $\overline{49}$ $\overline{148}$ $\overline{132}$

T Immediately afterward: Arch. . . . .
$\overline{136}$ $\overline{113}$ $\overline{97}$ $\overline{60}$ $\overline{43}$ $\overline{131}$ $\overline{142}$ $\overline{197}$

U Ship area: 2 wds. . . . .
$\overline{161}$ $\overline{133}$ $\overline{176}$ $\overline{74}$ $\overline{50}$ $\overline{198}$ $\overline{155}$ $\overline{7}$

V Feminine name . . . .
$\overline{71}$ $\overline{51}$ $\overline{168}$

W Single . . . .
$\overline{72}$ $\overline{44}$ $\overline{169}$

X "... I stood one morning in our _____ looking
down the street": Hyph. (301). . . . .
$\overline{26}$ $\overline{157}$ $\overline{83}$ $\overline{107}$ $\overline{15}$ $\overline{8}$ $\overline{137}$ $\overline{162}$ $\overline{149}$

Y Francis Prosper was certainly this . . . .
$\overline{45}$ $\overline{67}$ $\overline{203}$ $\overline{27}$

Z To issue, come forth . . . .
$\overline{201}$ $\overline{188}$ $\overline{61}$ $\overline{68}$ $\overline{92}$ $\overline{114}$ $\overline{75}$

Z₁ Pouting grimace: Fr. . . . .
$\overline{152}$ $\overline{9}$ $\overline{78}$ $\overline{204}$

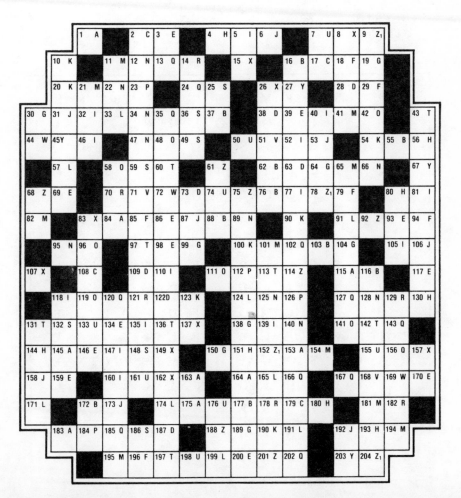

The Adventure of the Copper Beeches

34. Here's another of Mr. White's Word Detection puzzles. In this one, you'll only have to run down the words in the list—there's no Mystery Quotation.

Agency
Alcohol
Alice

Black Swan
Bradshaw

Carlo
Copper Beeches

Edward

Fowler

Governesses

Hair
Halifax
Hampshire
High Street

Jephro Rucastle

Mauritius
Montague Place

Nova Scotia

Philadelphia

Southampton
Spence Munro
Stoper

Toller

Violet Hunter

Walsall
Westaway's

```
S P E N C E M U N R O S T B K L
R H L A L C O H O L H W N X A I
Z I T V W A F S V D A A E M D Q
E L S B I K T I A L X N I R B C
H A A L R O O C S O U C A R L O
A D C W P B L A C K S W A N S P
M E U E G A L E O H D D P I X P
P L R S Q L E R T E S T W A I E
S P O T D I R U I H R A F E M R
H H R A U C M O A F U I B D C B
I I H W R E L W O F L N Y L R E
R A P A S O U T H A M P T O N E
E B E Y O H I G H S T R E E T C
Y U J S E S S E N R E V O G R H
A M X M O N T A G U E P L A C E
Y C N E G A Z M A U R I T I U S
```

35. In this cryptogramic comment upon the joys of nature, you will find no Js, Ks, Qs, Xs or Zs.

AOL SVDLZA HUK CPSLZA HSSLFZ PU SVUKVU KV UVA

WYLZLUA H TVYL KYLHKMBS YLJVYK VM ZPU AOHU KVLZ

AOL ZTPSPUN HUK ILHBAPMBS JVBUAYFZPKL.

36. Here are a number of Anagrams which don't have much to do with the people and places in our story which were scrambled up in order to create them. See if you can discover who or what they are anyway. The number of letters comprising each solution word is found in the parentheses adjoining each entry.

People		Places	
1. Oh, he'll reck moss.	(8, 6)	1. Tee Bert's ark.	(5, 6)
2. The run to evil	(6, 6)	2. Copps, he be Cree.	(6, 7)
3. Emu pens corn.	(6, 5)	3. All the wan bocks	(5, 4, 5)
4. Tails cure lace.	(5, 8)	4. Piled lip—Ha-ha!	(12)
5. Let cheap jurors	(6, 8)	5. Ug! Motets are ten.	(8, 6)
6. Rises stop'm	(4, 6)	6. Crew the sin.	(10)
7. Who jots Ann?	(4, 6)	7. Ooo! Darn that sump!	(11, 4)
8. Dewar's curd, et al.	(6, 8)	8. Ma! Her hips!	(9)

37. This Scramblegram has taken a comment Holmes makes to Watson on their way to the Copper Beeches and jostles it around. Your job is to put it back together again. Two hints may help: The sentence actually does begin with "I" and you should pay attention to that comma after "explanations." I withhold the period out of pure cussedness.

I KNOW EXPLANATIONS, COVER FACTS WHICH AS FAR SEPA-RATE THEM AS WE WOULD HAVE DEVISED EACH OF THE SEVEN

Silver Blaze

38. On to the turf, where Holmes masterminds one of his most thrilling adventures.

ACROSS

1 " 'I never had such a _____, sir,' answered the lady" (342)
5 Does a job on a manuscript
11 _____ Hill: Boston site
14 Famous horse, with 25 Down
15 "Someone's in the kitchen with _____"
16 Snakelike fishes
18 Comfort; freedom from pain
19 Med. specialty
21 Pain
22 _____ Grit: novel and film
23 Overhead railway, for short
24 Weep copiously
26 Minute particle
27 Continent: Abbr.
28 _____ I Lay Dying: Faulkner novel
30 ". . . an ivory-handled knife with a very delicate, inflexible _____" (342)
32 ". . . it was a rule that the _____ on duty should drink nothing else" (337)
34 ". . . Tavistock, which lies, like the _____ of a shield" (340)
36 Fill; gratify completely
37 Poetic contraction for unclose
38 It was curried (337)
41 Buddhist sect
42 Garden workman
43 "_____ la-la"
44 Brazilian soccer pro
46 _____ Andrews: "Mod Squad" star
49 Suffix denoting habitation
50 Landers or Southern
51 Employed for a purpose
53 Puzzle favorite: Abbr.
54 Actress _____ Merkel
57 Injure
60 Swiss sight
62 "The _____ Cup" (335)
64 "To _____ is human"
65 Ali's "_____-a-Dope"
67 "One man's _____ is another man's Persian"
68 Leave out
69 ". . . the favourite's _____ was empty" (338)
70 Biblical land
71 Northern Italian river
72 Do a sewing job
73 Shade tree
75 "_____ I walked out on the streets of Laredo"
77 Ireland
80 The god of physical love
82 _____ cummings
83 Aural protuberances
85 Spanish Mmes
86 Keep away
88 He didn't finish in the money (347)
90 Observe
91 Actor Bruce and family
92 H found it because he was looking for it (343)

DOWN

1 _____ M for Murder
2 Monogram of Mr. Hyde's creator
3 Adam and _____
4 Compass direction
5 Sellout signs
6 Responsible for 6 Across: Abbr.
7 Day: Sp.
8 ". . . the curious _____ of the dog in the night-time" (347)
9 Resort lake
10 Prefix for andoah and anigan?
11 Fishing boat necessity
12 Poetic contraction
13 "Because I made a _____, my dear Watson, . . . a more common occurrence than anyone would think" (336)
14 Watson often may _____, but he does not observe
17 China or Aegean
20 Newhart and Hope
25 See 14 Across
28 The Charles's dog
29 Attention-getting sound
31 Dined
32 Card game played with stakes and forfeits
33 Gorilla
34 NYC subway line

35 Possessive pronoun
39 The curry in 38 Across covered this up (338)
40 Seines
42 Stone_____, British tourist trap
45 Robert E. _____
47 Fleming, of Bondian fame
48 Chew, as a bone
52 "To _____; to King's Pyland" (335)
53 ". . . he will guard it as the _____ of his eye" (345)
54 Addict
55 Hunter (337)
56 Hewer
57 The _____ of Sherlock Holmes
58 The Greek tycoon

59 See 34 down
61 Mauna _____
63 Sch. in Dixie
66 French pronoun
68 Uncloses, poetically
69 "I'll show you how we _____ them in King's Pyland" (337)
72 "From _____ to toe"
74 Man's nickname
75 Region: tract
76 Euro-Asian Union: Abbr.
78 Female name
79 Compass direction
81 Religious crime
83 Feminine suffix
84 Fitting
87 Summer "time": Abbr.
89 _____ Housman

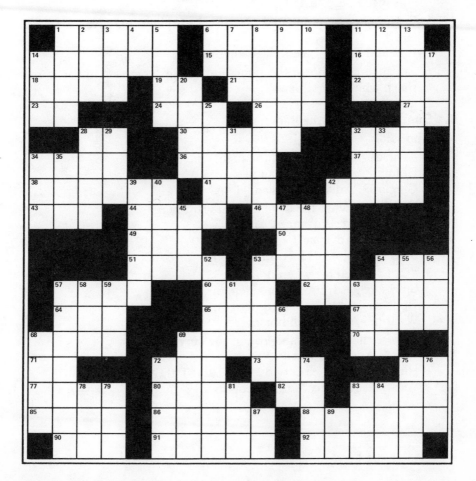

39. The Wessex Cup II. Here's a horse race of a different color. The grid on the bottom of the opposite page represents a racetrack. The six horses that ran in the Wessex Cup in our tale are lined up at the gate. Each square along the way represents one length. By answering the questions in the following three mini-quizzes correctly, the horses will end at the finish line in the proper order. Put an "X" in the squares to represent advances, all of which are for one length unless otherwise stated. Be careful: Some questions are tricky.

I. **Stumpers at the Gate**
   1. If Watson smoked a cigarette on his first trip to Colonel Ross's stables, advance all horses.
   If he smoked a cigar, advance only Desborough (D), Pugilist (P) and Silver Blaze (S).
   2. If the groom at Mapleford was named Dawson, advance Iris (I), P and Rasper (R).
   If not, advance D, R and The Negro (T).
   3. Advance I and S two lengths each if Simpson's cravat was red and black.
   Advance all horses one length if not.
   4. Advance all horses if the dress bill was over £30.
   Advance P, R and T if less.
   5. If Holmes complimented Gregory's imagination, advance D, R and T.
   If he didn't, advance R two lengths.
   6. Advance each horse the same number of lengths as there were sheep who went lame.

II. **Quotations Along the Backstretch**
   Who said:
   1. "The dog did nothing in the night-time." (347)
   Holmes?: Advance D, I and P
   Gregory?: Advance R, S and T
   2. "And you, what the devil do you want here?" (344)
   Ned Hunter?: Advance P and T
   Dawson?: Advance T three lengths
   Silas Brown?: Advance all horses
   3. "Can you tell me where I am?" (337)
   Simpson?: Advance P three lengths
   Holmes?: Advance T three lengths
   Watson?: Advance all horses
   4. "There they are, coming round the curve." (347)
   Ross?: Advance D and R
   Holmes?: Advance D two lengths and T three
   Watson?: Advance T three lengths

5. "So you're one of those damned touts!" (337)
Hunter?: Advance S two lengths, I three lengths and all others one
Silas?: Advance I three lengths, D, P and T one

6. "Go? Where to?" (335)
Gregory?: Advance all horses
Watson?: Advance I two lengths, S two and T three

III. Who's Who in the Home Stretch

1. Who first spotted Fitzroy?
Edith?: Advance R three and P one
Ethel?: Advance D four and R one

2. Who finished third?
Desborough?: Advance R two and T one
Iris?: Advance D four and P one
Rasper?: Advance I two and S one

3. Whose overcoat was on the furze-bush?
Simpson's?: Advance P two and T one
Straker's?: Advance P three and D one
Hunter's?: Advance I two and P three

4. Whodunit?
Ross?: Advance all horses
Simpson?: Advance R two and I one
Blaze?: Advance S three

One horse, and only one, should now have reached the finish line. The other five have lost by one, two, three or four lengths. Check the answer section to see if *your* horse came in.

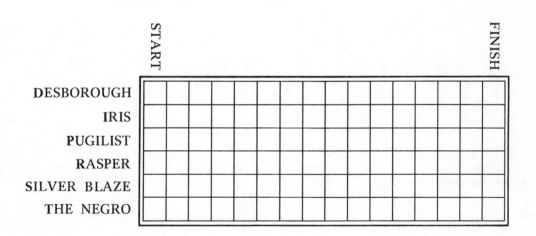

The Yellow Face

40. Holmes's petulance in the Clue Line gets its comeuppance in the Quotation in this Double-Crostic celebrating one of the Master's more risible failures.

Clues

A Nerve impulse transfer site . . . .
$\overline{127}$ $\overline{73}$ $\overline{68}$ $\overline{145}$ $\overline{92}$ $\overline{117}$ $\overline{56}$

B "I want your _____ as . . . a man of the world" (352) . . . .
$\overline{5}$ $\overline{74}$ $\overline{85}$ $\overline{131}$ $\overline{119}$ $\overline{34}$ $\overline{146}$

C. Obscure; vague . . . .
$\overline{42}$ $\overline{138}$ $\overline{149}$ $\overline{53}$ $\overline{123}$

D Suave . . . .
$\overline{35}$ $\overline{130}$ $\overline{167}$ $\overline{93}$ $\overline{6}$ $\overline{77}$

E "Our little place was very _____, considering it is so close to town" (353) . . . .
$\overline{100}$ $\overline{57}$ $\overline{177}$ $\overline{86}$ $\overline{36}$ $\overline{78}$ $\overline{30}$ $\overline{14}$ $\overline{94}$
$\overline{155}$ $\overline{110}$

F Munro's occupation: 2 wds. (352) . . . .
$\overline{105}$ $\overline{75}$ $\overline{128}$ $\overline{140}$ $\overline{111}$ $\overline{133}$ $\overline{61}$ $\overline{37}$ $\overline{101}$
$\overline{95}$ $\overline{54}$

G Posy-peddler. . . . .
$\overline{158}$ $\overline{55}$ $\overline{62}$ $\overline{114}$ $\overline{15}$ $\overline{7}$ $\overline{69}$

H ". . . his will . . . was _____ his inclinations" (352) .
$\overline{98}$ $\overline{24}$ $\overline{116}$ $\overline{29}$ $\overline{136}$ $\overline{70}$ $\overline{172}$ $\overline{159}$ $\overline{63}$
$\overline{43}$

I "Did she ever talk of _____ the place?" (358) . . . .
$\overline{144}$ $\overline{25}$ $\overline{58}$ $\overline{148}$ $\overline{79}$ $\overline{161}$ $\overline{16}$ $\overline{126}$ $\overline{71}$
$\overline{82}$

J Pub. . . . .
$\overline{8}$ $\overline{164}$ $\overline{44}$ $\overline{125}$ $\overline{80}$ $\overline{135}$ $\overline{17}$ $\overline{59}$

K Untrustworthy; financially unsound: 3 wds., Hyph . . . .
$\overline{64}$ $\overline{153}$ $\overline{141}$ $\overline{134}$ $\overline{165}$ $\overline{120}$ $\overline{9}$ $\overline{170}$ $\overline{18}$
$\overline{45}$

L The present . . . .
$\overline{46}$ $\overline{132}$ $\overline{10}$ $\overline{38}$ $\overline{175}$

M The Wizard of Menlo Park. . . . .
$\overline{142}$ $\overline{121}$ $\overline{47}$ $\overline{96}$ $\overline{19}$ $\overline{157}$

N Sit again . . . .
$\overline{26}$ $\overline{171}$ $\overline{102}$ $\overline{129}$ $\overline{99}$ $\overline{39}$

O ". . . trees are always a _____ kind of thing" (354) .
$\overline{48}$ $\overline{103}$ $\overline{40}$ $\overline{87}$ $\overline{11}$ $\overline{154}$ $\overline{166}$ $\overline{20}$ $\overline{60}$
$\overline{122}$ $\overline{137}$

P ". . . there came an ____ desire to see the child once more" (361) . . . .
$\overline{174}$ $\overline{115}$ $\overline{163}$ $\overline{81}$ $\overline{1}$ $\overline{150}$ $\overline{12}$ $\overline{88}$ $\overline{72}$

$\overline{65}$ $\overline{139}$ $\overline{49}$

Q According to Dr. Johnson, the principal sustenance of the Scot. . . . .
$\overline{176}$ $\overline{2}$ $\overline{97}$ $\overline{27}$

R Of the nose . . . .
$\overline{160}$ $\overline{41}$ $\overline{112}$ $\overline{106}$ $\overline{21}$

S Munro carried it with him to Baker Street (352) . .
$\overline{76}$ $\overline{13}$ $\overline{66}$ $\overline{89}$ $\overline{50}$ $\overline{124}$ $\overline{151}$ $\overline{31}$ $\overline{113}$

T Helpers . . . .
$\overline{143}$ $\overline{83}$ $\overline{22}$ $\overline{32}$ $\overline{90}$

U This characterized "the yellow face": 2 wds. (361) . . . .
$\overline{51}$ $\overline{156}$ $\overline{84}$ $\overline{169}$ $\overline{147}$ $\overline{3}$ $\overline{108}$ $\overline{107}$ $\overline{28}$

V Munro heard this singing in the cottage kitchen. . .
$\overline{118}$ $\overline{23}$ $\overline{104}$ $\overline{109}$ $\overline{168}$ $\overline{67}$

W Hairdresser, for one . . . .
$\overline{4}$ $\overline{173}$ $\overline{33}$ $\overline{152}$ $\overline{52}$ $\overline{91}$ $\overline{162}$

1 P	2 Q	3 U	4 W	5 B	6 D		7 G	8 J	9 K	10 L	
11 O	12 P		13 S	14 E		15 G	16 I		17 J	18 K	19 M	20 O	21 R
22 T		23 V	24 H	25 I	26 N		27 Q	28 U	29 H	30 E	31 S	32 T	
33 W	34 B	35 D		36 E	37 F	38 L	39 N		40 O		41 R	42 C	
43 H	44 J	45 K	46 L	47 M	48 O	49 P		50 S		51 U	52 W	53 C	54 F
55 G	56 A		57 E	58 I	59 J	60 O	61 F	62 G	63 H	64 K	65 P	66 S	67 V
68 A	69 G		70 H	71 I		72 P	73 A		74 B	75 F	76 S	77 D	78 E
79 I		80 J	81 P		82 I	83 T	84 U	85 B	86 E	87 O		88 P	89 S
90 T	91 W		92 A	93 D	94 E	95 F	96 M		97 Q	98 H		99 N	
100 E	101 F	102 N	103 O		104 V	105 F	106 R	107 U		108 U	109 V		110 E
111 F	112 R	113 S	114 G	115 P	116 H	117 A		118 V	119 B	120 K	121 M	122 O	123 C
	124 S	125 J	126 I	127 A	128 F	129 N	130 D		131 B	132 L	133 F	134 K	135 J
136 H	137 O		138 C	139 P		140 F	141 K		142 M	143 T	144 I		145 A
146 B	147 U		148 I		149 C	150 P	151 S	152 W	153 K		154 O	155 E	
156 U	157 M	158 G	159 H	160 R	161 I	162 W	163 P	164 J	165 K		166 O	167 D	168 V
	169 U	170 K	171 N	172 H		173 W	174 P		175 L	176 Q	177 E		

41. The melodrama runs high in this and the following two Quotations from our tale.

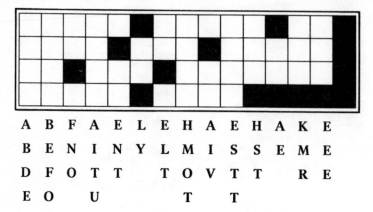

```
A  B  F  A  E  L  E  H  A  E  H  A  K  E
B  E  N  I  N  Y  L  M  I  S  S  E  M     E
D  F  O  T  T     T  O  V  T  T     R     E
E     O     U           T     T
```

42.

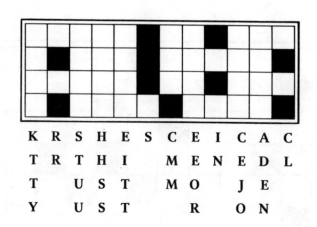

```
K  R  S  H  E  S  C  E  I  C  A  C
T  R  T  H  I     M  E  N  E  D  L
T     U  S  T     M  O     J  E
Y     U  S  T philia  R     O  N
```

43.

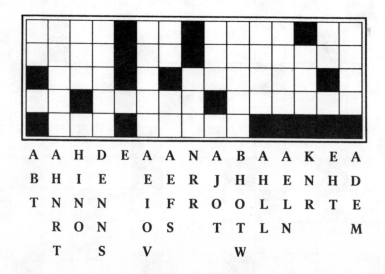

```
A  A  H  D  E  A  A  N  A  B  A  A  K  E  A
B  H  I  E     E  E  R  J  H  H  E  N  H  D
T  N  N     I  F  R  O  O  L  L  R  T     E
R  O  N     O  S     T  T  L  N           M
T     S     V        W
```

The Stock-broker's Clerk

44. A typical exchange between the Master's acuity and his Boswell's thoughts are presented below for your mystification.

```
Q  L  A  H  A  K  I  E  H  O  L  M  E  S  S
E  U  H  M  R  E  L  S  L  L  A  E  D  U  R
V  N  W  F  J  L  I  T  G  T  D  O  K  E  D
N  T  H  P  L  Y  T  S  I  E  C  Z  A  I  E
K  L  E  H  Q  E  R  O  U  O  O  S  H  F  L
H  I  N  R  L  U  S  K  M  D  O  G  T  S  D
T  B  S  E  I  H  T  T  E  N  U  A  D  O  L
W  Q  O  P  E  D  T  N  I  V  B  T  D  T  S
A  I  W  H  E  O  I  N  Y  N  W  E  P  F  G
S  T  A  A  Y  A  G  X  T  O  R  V  E  U  Y
O  Z  N  I  L  T  T  A  I  R  A  A  F  N  L
N  T  B  P  U  S  H  U  C  Q  R  H  T  W  E
C  C  X  D  O  B  E  N  I  Z  O  E  U  E  T
E  E  E  J  T  S  P  L  N  Y  O  C  L  A
H  C  D  O  H  E  E  R  P  G  Y  E  A  L  L
F  T  M  I  I  A  U  S  M  T  H  U  F  T  S
A  W  N  W  R  X  T  E  I  A  T  E  B  A  W
S  G  S  E  E  M  E  D  S  H  X  Z  M  L  R
N  K  A  J  L  E  X  I  Y  T  K  E  Q  R  E
L  P  E  R  C  E  I  V  E  N  E  O  X  T  P
I  A  U  N  V  N  U  J  M  R  L  I  T  E  A
```

1. 1-8-4-3-4-4-6-6
2. 4-3-7-9-3-5-6-10-6-4-2-3-4-9

45. A couple of Semi-Crostics from our tale.

Definitions	Words
He wore two faces	$\overline{13}\ \overline{32}\ \overline{1}\ \overline{16}\ \overline{12}\ \overline{31}$
_____-seven were fired from . . .	$\overline{10}\ \overline{3}\ \overline{25}\ \overline{28}\ \overline{33}\ \overline{4}$
Coxon & _____	$\overline{30}\ \overline{2}\ \overline{5}\ \overline{29}\ \overline{24}\ \overline{20}\ \overline{21}\ \overline{7}\ \overline{9}\ \overline{7}$
W bought his practice in this district	$\overline{13}\ \overline{27}\ \overline{29}\ \overline{29}\ \overline{34}\ \overline{35}\ \overline{36}\ \overline{22}\ \overline{14}\ \overline{1}$
Stock price Pycroft had to quote	$\overline{18}\ \overline{4}\ \overline{31}\ \overline{7}\ \overline{11}\ \overline{15}\ \overline{31}\ \overline{8}\ \overline{7}$
"You look remarkably _____ ": H to W	$\overline{31}\ \overline{20}\ \overline{19}\ \overline{6}\ \overline{7}\ \overline{23}$
Pycroft notices a gold one	$\overline{17}\ \overline{2}\ \overline{14}\ \overline{33}\ \overline{26}$

Solution:

$\overline{1}\ \ \overline{2}\ \ \overline{3}\ \ \ \overline{4}\ \ \overline{5}\ \ \overline{6}\ \ \ \overline{7}\ \ \overline{8}\ \ \overline{9}\ \ \ \overline{10}\ \overline{11}\ \overline{12}\ \ \ \overline{13}\ \overline{14}\ \overline{15}\ \overline{16}\ \overline{17}$

$\overline{18}\ \overline{19}\ \overline{20}\ \overline{21}\ \overline{22}\ \ \ \overline{23}\ \overline{24}\ \overline{25}\ \ \ \overline{26}\ \overline{27}\ \overline{28}\ \overline{29}\ \overline{30}\ \overline{31}\ \overline{32}\ \overline{33}\ \overline{34}\ \overline{35}\ \overline{36}.$

46.

Definitions	Words
Hall Pycroft, to H	$\overline{6}\ \overline{34}\ \overline{36}\ \overline{41}\ \overline{18}\ \overline{23}$
"We can only offer you a _____ 500"	$\overline{25}\ \overline{40}\ \overline{3}\ \overline{3}\ \overline{22}\ \overline{13}\ \overline{15}\ \overline{2}$
Franco-Midland _____ Company	$\overline{21}\ \overline{22}\ \overline{7}\ \overline{10}\ \overline{20}\ \overline{24}\ \overline{13}\ \overline{35}$
Where he had to go to report	$\overline{30}\ \overline{27}\ \overline{7}\ \overline{1}\ \overline{16}\ \overline{28}\ \overline{3}\ \overline{21}\ \overline{24}\ \overline{1}$
The hour Mawson's closed on Sat.	$\overline{19}\ \overline{20}\ \overline{38}\ \overline{26}\ \overline{37}\ \overline{32}$
H pretended to be one	$\overline{22}\ \overline{6}\ \overline{14}\ \overline{4}\ \overline{12}\ \overline{42}\ \overline{33}\ \overline{24}\ \overline{18}\ \overline{23}$
The _____ Standard	$\overline{31}\ \overline{37}\ \overline{17}\ \overline{28}\ \overline{8}\ \overline{42}\ \overline{3}$
The killer	$\overline{39}\ \overline{9}\ \overline{29}\ \overline{5}\ \overline{36}\ \overline{18}\ \overline{3}\ \overline{19}\ \overline{11}\ \overline{42}$

Solution:

"$\overline{1}\ \ \overline{2}\ \ \ \overline{3}\ \ \overline{4}\ \ \overline{5}$," $\overline{6}\ \ \overline{7}\ \ \overline{8}\ \ \overline{9}\ \ \overline{10}\ \ \ \overline{11}\ \overline{12}\ \overline{13}\ \ \ \overline{14}\ \overline{15}\ \overline{16}\ \overline{17}\ \overline{18}\ \overline{19}$,

"$\overline{20}\ \overline{21}\ \overline{22}\ \overline{23}\ \ \ \overline{24}\ \ \overline{25}\ \overline{26}\ \overline{27}\ \overline{28}\ \overline{29}\ \ \ \overline{30}\ \overline{31}\ \overline{32}\ \overline{33}\ \overline{34}\ \overline{35}\ \ \ \overline{36}\ \ \overline{37}\ \overline{38}$,

$\overline{39}\ \overline{40}\ \overline{41}\ \overline{42}$."

47. Here's the first of several groups of codes. Each one conveys a hidden message, though not from our tale. Good luck!

You think clearly only when you have difficult tasks to do. So read this with the mind on "story line," ok? And I guarantee you'll manage to solve, in minutes, this very elementary code.

48. "Tell Hudson I'll step out now. Everyone wants only noticing today. Bet Elly's sitting outside. Elly's always standing yare."

49. CAUTLAYLMILPYANIWGTIYHUO.

50. 16-18-15-21-4-12-25   17-19-6-20-6-15-21-10-15-8   1-17-23:

51. SS102D2/SS113/SF18A2/SF2
SB1-146/OP43A3/SB2-38D5/BC19/SB3-16A3
YF51/GS26/SS39D6/SS36/SF27D3

52. I love this Quotation. It's positively Shakespearean in its robustness. It's accompanied by a bass drum in the Clue Line. Wonderful fun marking the Master's first case.

Clues

A "We had no difficulty in losing our former ____" (385) . . . .

$\overline{81}$ $\overline{133}$ $\overline{114}$ $\overline{1}$ $\overline{17}$ $\overline{91}$ $\overline{156}$ $\overline{120}$ $\overline{184}$

$\overline{197}$

B "... my ____ sealed forever in death" (381) . . . .

$\overline{110}$ $\overline{2}$ $\overline{82}$ $\overline{52}$ $\overline{127}$ $\overline{115}$

C "There was excellent ____ shooting in the fens": Hyph. (374). . . . .

$\overline{3}$ $\overline{138}$ $\overline{18}$ $\overline{40}$ $\overline{100}$ $\overline{160}$ $\overline{70}$ $\overline{93}$

D "... to recompense them for the ____" (378) . . .

$\overline{105}$ $\overline{92}$ $\overline{150}$ $\overline{41}$ $\overline{4}$ $\overline{142}$ $\overline{139}$ $\overline{143}$ $\overline{111}$

E What the chaplain was (383) . . . .

$\overline{192}$ $\overline{25}$ $\overline{42}$ $\overline{164}$

F "____ and nail" . . . .

$\overline{116}$ $\overline{5}$ $\overline{53}$ $\overline{106}$ $\overline{33}$

G "... I heard Mr. Trevor make a sort of ____ noise in his throat (376). . . . .

$\overline{87}$ $\overline{19}$ $\overline{193}$ $\overline{35}$ $\overline{34}$ $\overline{6}$ $\overline{83}$ $\overline{71}$ $\overline{54}$

$\overline{43}$ $\overline{96}$

H He was attacked by the poaching gang: Full name (375) . . . .

$\overline{72}$ $\overline{121}$ $\overline{59}$ $\overline{26}$ $\overline{158}$ $\overline{7}$ $\overline{180}$ $\overline{36}$ $\overline{117}$

$\overline{128}$ $\overline{44}$

I "I'm just off a two-yearer in an ____ tramp": Hyph. (377). . . . .

$\overline{60}$ $\overline{84}$ $\overline{107}$ $\overline{97}$ $\overline{27}$ $\overline{20}$ $\overline{55}$ $\overline{8}$ $\overline{45}$

J Knobs; protuberances. . . . .

$\overline{9}$ $\overline{98}$ $\overline{122}$ $\overline{21}$ $\overline{73}$

K "... this is the message which struck ... Trevor ____ horror when he read it": 2 wds. (374) . . . . .

$\overline{112}$ $\overline{88}$ $\overline{28}$ $\overline{129}$ $\overline{167}$ $\overline{94}$ $\overline{10}$ $\overline{46}$

L Victor Trevor, to H: 2 wds. (374). . . . .

$\overline{74}$ $\overline{85}$ $\overline{22}$ $\overline{130}$ $\overline{186}$ $\overline{179}$ $\overline{47}$ $\overline{118}$ $\overline{95}$

$\overline{189}$

M Drift gently . . . .

$\overline{176}$ $\overline{99}$ $\overline{101}$ $\overline{61}$ $\overline{11}$

N Opposable digit. . . . .

$\overline{177}$ $\overline{12}$ $\overline{75}$ $\overline{29}$ $\overline{66}$

O "... and me still picking salt meat out of the ____": 2 wds. (377) . . . .

$\overline{144}$ $\overline{30}$ $\overline{62}$ $\overline{48}$ $\overline{123}$ $\overline{89}$ $\overline{159}$ $\overline{134}$ $\overline{151}$

$\overline{183}$ $\overline{174}$

P "As I glanced up from reading this ____ message" (374) . . . .

$\overline{178}$ $\overline{31}$ $\overline{13}$ $\overline{49}$ $\overline{196}$ $\overline{154}$ $\overline{76}$ $\overline{145}$ $\overline{161}$

$\overline{165}$ $\overline{169}$

Q Horrible; nightmarish . . . .

$\overline{56}$ $\overline{63}$ $\overline{131}$ $\overline{37}$ $\overline{170}$ $\overline{50}$ $\overline{77}$ $\overline{190}$

R Flowered necklaces . . . .
$\overline{38}$ $\overline{157}$ $\overline{78}$ $\overline{51}$

S Midwesterner . . . .
$\overline{135}$ $\overline{162}$ $\overline{64}$ $\overline{173}$ $\overline{163}$ $\overline{14}$

T "... how could he have fallen into the clutches of such a _____ !" (378) . . . .
$\overline{67}$ $\overline{195}$ $\overline{102}$ $\overline{136}$ $\overline{181}$ $\overline{175}$ $\overline{124}$

U "... he knew that the danger from Hudson had become _____" (380) . . . .
$\overline{191}$ $\overline{125}$ $\overline{182}$ $\overline{168}$ $\overline{146}$ $\overline{68}$ $\overline{166}$ $\overline{57}$

V For this case only: Lat., 2 wds. . . . .
$\overline{103}$ $\overline{39}$ $\overline{194}$ $\overline{58}$ $\overline{147}$

W Classic American Musical: 2 wds. . . . .
$\overline{65}$ $\overline{148}$ $\overline{126}$ $\overline{32}$ $\overline{113}$ $\overline{140}$ $\overline{187}$ $\overline{79}$

X Shirt accessories: 2 wds. . . . .
$\overline{152}$ $\overline{108}$ $\overline{137}$ $\overline{141}$ $\overline{132}$ $\overline{149}$ $\overline{188}$ $\overline{15}$ $\overline{155}$

Y Weasel and mink relative. . . . .
$\overline{153}$ $\overline{80}$ $\overline{90}$ $\overline{69}$ $\overline{104}$

Z "_____ Remember": *Fantasticks* theme, 2 wds. . . . .
$\overline{86}$ $\overline{119}$ $\overline{23}$ $\overline{109}$ $\overline{172}$

Z_1 Prepare land for crops . . . .
$\overline{24}$ $\overline{16}$ $\overline{171}$ $\overline{185}$

1 A	2 B	3 C		4 D	5 F	6 G		7 H	8 I	9 J	10 K
	11 M	12 N	13 P	14 S	15 X		16 Z_1	17 A		18 C	19 G	20 I	21 J	22 L	23 Z
	24 Z_1	25 E	26 H	27 I		28 K		29 N	30 O	31 P		32 W	33 F	34 G	
35 G	36 H	37 Q	38 R	39 V		40 C	41 D		42 E	43 G	44 H	45 I	46 K	47 L	48 O
49 P		50 Q	51 R		52 B	53 F	54 G	55 I	56 Q		57 U	58 V		59 H	60 I
61 M	62 O		63 Q	64 S	65 W		66 N	67 T	68 U	69 Y	70 C	71 G	72 H	73 J	
74 L	75 N	76 P		77 Q	78 R	79 W	80 Y	81 A	82 B	83 G		84 I	85 L		86 Z
87 G	88 K		89 O	90 Y	91 A	92 D	93 C	94 K	95 L	96 G		97 I	98 J	99 M	100 C
	101 M	102 T		103 V		104 Y	105 D	106 F	—	107 I	108 X	109 Z	110 B	111 D	112 K
	113 W	114 A	115 B	116 F	117 H	118 L	—	119 Z	120 A	121 H	122 J	123 O	124 T		125 U
126 W	127 B	128 H	129 K	130 L		131 Q	132 X	133 A		134 O	135 S	136 T	137 X	138 C	139 D
	140 W	141 X		142 D		143 D	144 O	145 P	146 U		147 V	148 W	149 X	150 D	151 O
	152 X	153 Y	154 P	155 X	156 A	157 R	158 H		159 O	160 C	161 P	162 S		163 S	
164 E	165 P	166 U		167 K	168 U	169 P	170 Q		171 Z_1	172 Z	173 S	174 O		175 T	176 M
177 N	178 P	179 L		180 H	181 T	182 U	183 O	184 A	185 Z_1	186 L		187 W	188 X	189 L
	190 Q	191 U	192 E		193 G	194 V	195 T	196 P	197 A					

The Musgrave Ritual

53. Holmes's second case owes as much for its existence to Musgrave's denseness and the villain's faulty choice of a moll as it does to Holmes's semi-effective efforts.

ACROSS

1 "Under the _____": part of 4 Down (392)
4 _____ up: prepared to drive
8 Army rank: Abbr.
11 Symbolized by the design in this puzzle (397)
15 White; graying, as in _____ frost
16 _____ Well That Ends Well
18 "Thanks _____ much": 2 wds.
19 Exxon, in the old days
20 Iranian monetary unit
21 Compass direction
22 Airport abbreviation
23 He kept it in his slipper (386)
25 "And _____ to bed": Pepysian style
26 Dog
28 Hang back
29 Odious army duty
30 Zoo "homes"
34 "Whose _____?": part of 4 Down, 2 wds. (392)
36 Sailor: Sl.
38 Scent
39 Traveling; expanding
40 Thirties agency initials
42 Neither partner
43 "Who's _____?": Abbott & Costello routine, 2 wds.
45 Actress _____ Merkel
47 _____ de coeur: Gallic expression of anguish
48 "_____ the World Turns": soap opera
49 Man's nickname
50 Compass direction
51 Norse goddess of death
52 _____ dog: early psychology subject
56 Cigarette by-product
57 Treasure Island monogram
59 Hell hath no greater fury than she (389)
60 Pretty; nice: Fr.
61 "Week _____ Glance": calendar booklets, 2 wds.
63 Dolts; idiots: Sl.
64 Thick; crowded
65 Pronoun: Fr.
67 Prefix for corn or sex

69 Roman god of the lower world
70 Film director Griffith
71 Prospero's daughter: The Tempest
74 Poetic homonym for 74 Down
75 "Izzat _____?"
77 Arabian ruler or prince
78 Light tan
80 "Our chambers were always full of chemicals and of criminal _____" (386)
82 A delicate color or hue
83 Greek porch
84 A set form or observation
85 Technical directors: Abbr.
86 The linden tree
87 Mister Zero, for short

DOWN

1 East of _____: Steinbeck novel
2 "_____, love, laugh and be happy"
3 _____ West, of Chickadee fame
4 "Whose was it?" etc.: 3 wds.
5 Greek goddess of dawn
6 Sunrise direction
7 Let run from the mouth, as tobacco juice
8 "But this _____ has one fault" (389)
9 Parisian cop
10 Abrupt, sharp sound
12 ". . . he affected a certain quiet primness of _____" (386)
13 This: Span.
14 Flightless bird of New Zealand
17 "_____ the pigs": feeding time
24 "She had flung into the lake a _____ containing" (392)
26 "_____ help you": salesman's request, 2 wds.
27 Muckraker Jacob _____
30 Large shell
31 Lover
32 King Kong, for one
33 Comparative suffix
34 Female service acronym
35 Explosive
37 The butler did it: his name?
39 Hospital personnel: Abbr.
41 ". . . you should add this case to your _____" (387)

43 "Over the _____": part of 4 Down
44 Not present: Abbr.
46 Mountaintop home
49 Senator Dirkson's, familiarly
52 Solar _____s, Sherlockian pretender
53 Mystified; wide-eyed
54 Academic degrees
55 Chemical suffixes
58 The true owners of the bounty (397)
60 Month: Abbr.
62 Female name
64 What "I" did "in marble halls"

65 ". . . and then _____ a man who had no feet": 2 wds.
66 "But with me there is a _____" (386)
68 That is: Lat.
70 Three: Ger.
72 Peel
73 *Entr'_____*
74 "To _____ is human"
75 ". . . my client led me away . . . to the _____ on the lawn where the elm had stood" (393)
76 European Capital
79 King: Fr.
81 Element-ary suffix

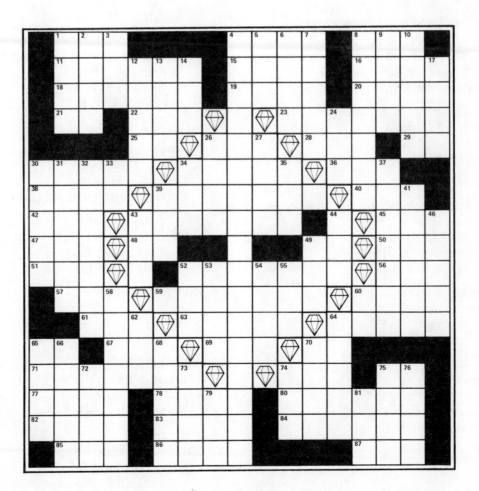

54. I call this a "Quaze"—half quiz, half maze. It's also a treasure hunt. By choosing the correct answer to each question, and filling in the correct squares (in the grid on the opposite page) indicated by those answers, you will be brought from the starting square, already filled in for you in the upper left-hand corner, to the finish, where your final "X" will mark the "Treasure" spot. Move with reference to the last square occupied, in the six compass directions given. (If the answer to the first question, for instance, instructs you to move SE-3, you would fill in the first three squares diagonally downward from the last one occupied, or southeast.) Six of the 22 questions aren't questions at all, but merely directions to follow in completing the maze. Hint: The line of the maze never crosses itself. See the answer section to check your final "X" and your route against mine. (Don't count the square you are starting on.)

1. What did Holmes store in the "toe end of a Persian slipper?"
   Cigars: SE-6
   Tobacco: SE-4
   Correspondence: SE-2

2. NE-1

3. What particularly annoyed Watson about Holmes's housekeeping?
   Mountains of documents: N-2; E-4
   Chemical fumes: N-1; E-6
   Scattered mementos: SE-1; NE-3

4. Holmes's storage box was constructed of
   Steel: S-5; NW-1
   Wood: S-3; NW-1
   Tin: SE-1; SW-4

5. W-4; S-2

6. What was Ricoletti's plaint (besides an "abominable wife")?
   Gout: E-4
   Rheumatism: E-3; S-1
   Club-foot: E-5; NE-3

7. Which was *not* a relic from "The Musgrave Ritual?"
   Brass key: N-1; NE-2
   Oil-stained cloth: N-1; NE-4
   Metal disks: S-1; N-5

8. Where did Holmes first live in London?
   Montague Street: E-5; SW-2
   Mulberry Street: E-2; S-2
   Pall Mall: E-3; S-4

9. W-2; SW-4

10. _____ Musgrave, Holmes's college friend:
    Rodney: S-4; E-3
    Raleigh: S-3; W-2
    Reginald: S-2; SW-2

11. The family estate?
    Burlstone: W-2; S-1
    Murlstone: W-4; S-1
    Hurlstone: W-2; SW-3

12. Brunton's tenure with the Musgraves?
    7 years: N-2; W-2
    15 years: N-3; W-4
    20 years: NW-1; N-2

13. W-1; SW-2

14. It kept Musgrave awake.
    Noises in the night: S-4; E-2
    Café noir: SE-4
    Curried mutton: SE-4; NE-2

15. "Where was the sun?"
    Over the oak: NE-4; E-3
    Over the elm: NE-5; S-1
    Over the hill: NE-3; S-2

16. How high was the elm?
    36 feet: S-4; NE-6
    64 feet: NE-3; N-3
    72 feet: NE-5; N-1

17. What was found first at the murder scene?
    Brunton's muffler: NE-2; E-3
    Brunton's gloves: S-2; E-3
    Brunton's boots: S-1; E-4

18. Whodunit?
    Janet Tregellis: S-4; SW-2
    Rachel Howells: S-5; SW-2
    Musgrave: S-6; SW-2

19. W-2; S-2

20. In whose reign were the jewels hidden?
    James I: S-2; W-2
    Charles I: S-3; W-3
    Charles II: S-2; W-2
    None of the above: SW-4; S-2

21. In the canonical chronology, which
    case is this for Holmes?
    First: E-2; NE-1
    Second: E-5; NE-1
    Third: E-6; NE-1

22. E-1; SE-1

. . . and so under.

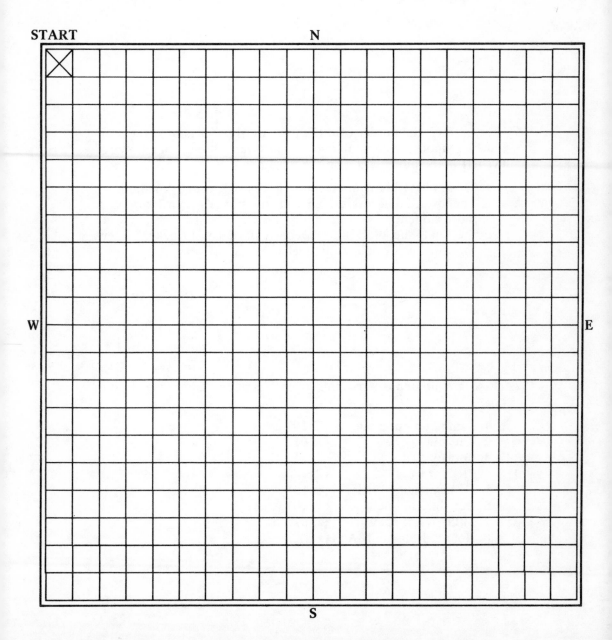

The Reigate Puzzle

55. A Holmesian maxim. Hint: A=P

NE ND JK EMT MNLMTDE NHAJCEPIRT NI EMT PCE JK

STETRENJI EJ QT PQGT EJ CTRJLINUT JZE JK P

IZHQTC JK KPRED, XMNRM PCT NIRNSTIEPG PIS

XMNRM YNEPG.

56. Here, in ascending order of difficulty, are three Scramblegrams, all touching upon the "scrambling" Holmes went through in our story. I've left in the punctuation on the third one.

    a. There I have his madness found in that was usually method
    b. The dreadful face assumed had my friend's poor expression most suddenly
    c. the kind. slip of Holmes keenly pained any mistake, I knew for how I was would at the feel

57. These are nonsense Anagrams from characters mentioned in our tale.

    1. I am not a purer bus.   (5, 10)
    2. The lonely Cora   (7, 6)
    3. Coolant "D"   (3, 5)
    4. "R" for trees   (9)
    5. M! I can hang, Uncle!   (4, 10)
    6. Doc, hangin'l num.   (3, 10)
    7. I kill—Wam!—in war.   (7, 6)
    8. No, sir! Rome in N.A.   (5,8)

The Crooked Man

58. Watson's old sweet song.

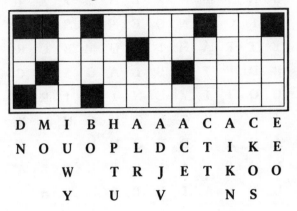

```
D M I B H A A A C A C E
N O U O P L D C T I K E
    W   T R J E T K O O
    Y   U V     N S
```

59. The ould sod.

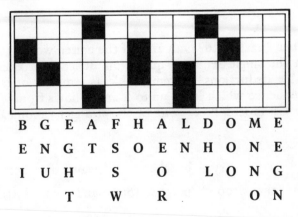

```
B G E A F H A L D O M E
E N G T S O E N H O N E
I U H   S O   L O N G
    T   W R       O N
```

60. A classic exchange, with an added challenge of punctuation to fill in.

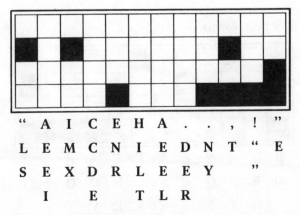

```
" A I C E H A . . , ! "
L E M C N I E D N T " E
S E X D R L E E Y     "
    I   E   T L R
```

The Resident Patient

61. Just a single Hidden Phrase for you to find in this one.

```
A H T E M A N S O I E Y
S N T F O P L A C E X J
S F O U N D E N A S I H
E T E A H I L O M S U R
R D F T T B L A O S E C
U O T I Z E N I N I R T
T Y G R G Y O R G H V K
A H X P D N Q U D W R A
N O I T A I C E R P P A
U F L A I E T B N S H T
```

12-2-6-5-2-5-5-3-4-5.

62. Remember Puzzle #20? Only one of the paired words below is used to form the single sentence quotation. It's one of Holmes's more remarkable deductions—so remarkable as a matter of fact that the whole sequence which leads up to it and follows from it is repeated in "The Cardboard Box"—one of the stranger canonical eccentricities.

It	can	do	a	very	beeches	way	if	here	a	begin.
She	does	seem	the	too	preposterous	and	of	settling	I	dispute.

—— —— —— —— —— ————— —— — ———— — ————.

63. Me, I collect tapeworms.

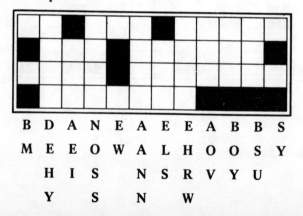

```
B D A N E A E E A B B S
M E E O W A L H O O S Y
  H I S   N S R V Y U
  Y   S   N   W
```

The Greek Interpreter

64. A couple of incisive Semi-Crostics on the importance of heredity, to commemorate the introduction of sibling rivalry into the Canon.

Definitions	Words
The villain: Full name	$\overline{7}$ $\overline{1}$ $\overline{2}$ $\overline{23}$ $\overline{10}$ $\overline{13}$ $\overline{20}$ $\overline{18}$ $\overline{32}$ $\overline{14}$ $\overline{43}$ $\overline{37}$ $\overline{42}$
The Greek interpreter	$\overline{43}$ $\overline{37}$ $\overline{16}$ $\overline{25}$ $\overline{31}$
Where the villain pretended to take the interpreter	$\overline{26}$ $\overline{21}$ $\overline{5}$ $\overline{15}$ $\overline{4}$ $\overline{35}$ $\overline{36}$ $\overline{39}$ $\overline{11}$ $\overline{5}$
The victim . . .	$\overline{26}$ $\overline{33}$ $\overline{34}$ $\overline{28}$ $\overline{17}$ $\overline{13}$ $\overline{30}$ $\overline{38}$
. . . who was technically this . . .	$\overline{29}$ $\overline{41}$ $\overline{44}$ $\overline{24}$ $\overline{1}$ $\overline{36}$ $\overline{27}$
. . . and was certainly this	$\overline{9}$ $\overline{18}$ $\overline{6}$ $\overline{22}$ $\overline{8}$ $\overline{33}$ $\overline{21}$ $\overline{13}$
Chaucer's "The Wife _____": 2 wds.	$\overline{12}$ $\overline{40}$ $\overline{19}$ $\overline{25}$ $\overline{3}$ $\overline{7}$

Solution:

$\overline{1}$ $\overline{2}$ $\overline{3}$ $\overline{4}$ $\overline{5}$ $\overline{6}$ $\overline{7}$ $\overline{8}$ $\overline{9}$ $\overline{10}$ $\overline{11}$ $\overline{12}$ $\overline{13}$ $\overline{14}$ $\overline{15}$

$\overline{16}$ $\overline{17}$ $\overline{18}$ $\overline{19}$ $\overline{20}$ $\overline{21}$ $\overline{22}$ $\overline{23}$ $\overline{24}$ $\overline{25}$ $\overline{26}$ $\overline{27}$ $\overline{28}$ $\overline{29}$ $\overline{30}$

$\overline{31}$ $\overline{32}$ $\overline{33}$ $\overline{34}$ $\overline{35}$ $\overline{36}$ $\overline{37}$ $\overline{38}$ $\overline{39}$ $\overline{40}$ $\overline{41}$ $\overline{42}$ $\overline{43}$ $\overline{44}$

65.

Definitions	Words
SH's Smarter Brother	$\overline{31}$ $\overline{23}$ $\overline{7}$ $\overline{21}$ $\overline{6}$ $\overline{25}$ $\overline{15}$
The _____ Club	$\overline{38}$ $\overline{37}$ $\overline{24}$ $\overline{22}$ $\overline{18}$ $\overline{19}$ $\overline{28}$ $\overline{35}$
Pall _____, where the brother lived	$\overline{39}$ $\overline{30}$ $\overline{14}$ $\overline{5}$
_____ Artillery, H fancied	$\overline{42}$ $\overline{43}$ $\overline{40}$ $\overline{36}$ $\overline{33}$
_____ Cross Station	$\overline{41}$ $\overline{9}$ $\overline{10}$ $\overline{42}$ $\overline{37}$ $\overline{19}$ $\overline{22}$
Where Sophy lived: 2 wds.	$\overline{45}$ $\overline{2}$ $\overline{3}$ $\overline{39}$ $\overline{34}$ $\overline{4}$ $\overline{26}$ $\overline{13}$ $\overline{20}$ $\overline{11}$
Where the victim was from	$\overline{12}$ $\overline{45}$ $\overline{16}$ $\overline{17}$ $\overline{19}$ $\overline{1}$
A long walk	$\overline{27}$ $\overline{32}$ $\overline{8}$ $\overline{3}$
Opposite of "on"	$\overline{43}$ $\overline{29}$ $\overline{44}$

Solution:

"$\overline{1}$ $\overline{2}$ $\overline{3}$ $\overline{4}$ $\overline{5}$ $\overline{6}$ $\overline{7}$ $\overline{8}$ $\overline{9}$ $\overline{10}$ $\overline{11}$ $\overline{12}$ $\overline{13}$ $\overline{14}$ $\overline{15}$ $\overline{16}$ $\overline{17}$

$\overline{18}$ $\overline{19}$ $\overline{20}$ $\overline{21}$ $\overline{22}$ $\overline{23}$ $\overline{24}$ $\overline{25}$ $\overline{26}$ $\overline{27}$ $\overline{28}$ $\overline{29}$ $\overline{30}$ $\overline{31}$ $\overline{32}$ $\overline{33}$ $\overline{34}$,"

$\overline{35}$ $\overline{36}$ $\overline{37}$ $\overline{38}$ $\overline{39}$ $\overline{40}$ $\overline{41}$ $\overline{42}$ $\overline{43}$ $\overline{44}$ $\overline{45}$

66. Brother Mycroft is introduced to the Canon and explanations are in order.

Clues

A "_____ cow": elocutionary nonsense, 3 wds. . . . .
$\overline{79}$ $\overline{86}$ $\overline{12}$ $\overline{74}$ $\overline{116}$ $\overline{131}$ $\overline{28}$ $\overline{136}$ $\overline{178}$
$\overline{154}$ $\overline{126}$

B "It seems obvious that your faculty of _____ is due to your own systematic training" (435) . . . .
$\overline{132}$ $\overline{50}$ $\overline{29}$ $\overline{75}$ $\overline{155}$ $\overline{182}$ $\overline{13}$ $\overline{87}$ $\overline{1}$
$\overline{172}$ $\overline{162}$

C Where Mycroft works (436). . . . .
$\overline{81}$ $\overline{99}$ $\overline{47}$ $\overline{163}$ $\overline{30}$ $\overline{160}$ $\overline{103}$ $\overline{121}$ $\overline{175}$

D Shoemaker. . . . .
$\overline{144}$ $\overline{48}$ $\overline{62}$ $\overline{174}$ $\overline{189}$ $\overline{80}$ $\overline{31}$

E Unprepared; without warning: 2 wds. . . . .
$\overline{145}$ $\overline{98}$ $\overline{111}$ $\overline{193}$ $\overline{51}$ $\overline{33}$ $\overline{76}$ $\overline{43}$

F ". . . some from shyness, some from _____" (436) .
$\overline{61}$ $\overline{82}$ $\overline{2}$ $\overline{128}$ $\overline{49}$ $\overline{34}$ $\overline{184}$ $\overline{171}$ $\overline{93}$
$\overline{19}$ $\overline{104}$

G Do a job on a manuscript . . . .
$\overline{20}$ $\overline{149}$ $\overline{35}$ $\overline{105}$

H Paul's sister (441) . . . .
$\overline{14}$ $\overline{94}$ $\overline{179}$ $\overline{168}$ $\overline{112}$

I "This reticence upon his part had increased the somewhat _____ effect which he produced upon me" (435) . . . .
$\overline{63}$ $\overline{146}$ $\overline{113}$ $\overline{95}$ $\overline{15}$ $\overline{3}$ $\overline{129}$

J Rope game: 3 wds. . . . .
$\overline{52}$ $\overline{44}$ $\overline{77}$ $\overline{36}$ $\overline{190}$ $\overline{117}$ $\overline{137}$ $\overline{21}$

K Commandments or Little Indians . . . .
$\overline{64}$ $\overline{150}$ $\overline{37}$

L Biblical tribesman . . . .
$\overline{53}$ $\overline{4}$ $\overline{96}$ $\overline{138}$ $\overline{22}$ $\overline{177}$ $\overline{88}$

M Opposed; in conflict: 2 wds. . . . .
$\overline{38}$ $\overline{195}$ $\overline{97}$ $\overline{5}$ $\overline{130}$ $\overline{57}$

N Leg part. . . . .
$\overline{6}$ $\overline{139}$ $\overline{65}$ $\overline{158}$ $\overline{194}$

O Cowled . . . .
$\overline{7}$ $\overline{106}$ $\overline{66}$ $\overline{135}$ $\overline{54}$ $\overline{153}$

P _____ Blue Men: Roueché classic. . . . .
$\overline{140}$ $\overline{83}$ $\overline{152}$ $\overline{32}$ $\overline{176}$ $\overline{39}$

Q At accord with: 3 wds. . . . .
$\overline{100}$ $\overline{67}$ $\overline{159}$ $\overline{122}$ $\overline{58}$ $\overline{183}$ $\overline{167}$ $\overline{23}$

R Mycroft's "seniority": 2 wds. . . . .
$\overline{101}$ $\overline{166}$ $\overline{89}$ $\overline{169}$ $\overline{118}$ $\overline{16}$ $\overline{188}$ $\overline{8}$ $\overline{141}$
$\overline{119}$

S Descriptive of Diogenes Club members (436) . . . .
$\overline{173}$ $\overline{157}$ $\overline{17}$ $\overline{59}$ $\overline{45}$ $\overline{114}$ $\overline{68}$ $\overline{142}$ $\overline{84}$
$\overline{90}$

T "... his strange, catchy little laugh was also a
symptom of some _____": 2 wds. (441) . . . .

$\overline{69}$ $\overline{143}$ $\overline{24}$ $\overline{107}$ $\overline{120}$ $\overline{18}$ $\overline{115}$ $\overline{186}$ $\overline{164}$

$\overline{134}$ $\overline{161}$ $\overline{40}$ $\overline{78}$

U The victim (440) . . . .

$\overline{165}$ $\overline{151}$ $\overline{60}$ $\overline{9}$ $\overline{25}$ $\overline{41}$ $\overline{108}$ $\overline{127}$

V "... his little pointed beard was thready and
ill-_____" (441) . . . .

$\overline{26}$ $\overline{181}$ $\overline{133}$ $\overline{109}$ $\overline{124}$ $\overline{187}$ $\overline{10}$ $\overline{42}$ $\overline{70}$

W Constellation . . . .

$\overline{27}$ $\overline{180}$ $\overline{110}$ $\overline{125}$ $\overline{71}$

X Twist; contort, as in agony . . . .

$\overline{102}$ $\overline{191}$ $\overline{148}$ $\overline{170}$ $\overline{55}$ $\overline{11}$

Y "... our friend who ... began these _____ has been
forced to return to the East" (441) . . . .

$\overline{85}$ $\overline{73}$ $\overline{92}$ $\overline{72}$ $\overline{46}$ $\overline{185}$ $\overline{56}$ $\overline{123}$ $\overline{192}$

$\overline{156}$ $\overline{91}$ $\overline{147}$

1 B		2 F	3 I	4 L	5 M					
	6 N	7 O	8 R	9 U		10 V	11 X		12 A	13 B	14 H
15 I	16 R		17 S	18 T	19 F	20 G	21 J	22 L	23 Q	24 T		25 U	26 V
27 W	28 A	29 B	30 C	31 D	32 P	33 E	34 F	35 G	36 J	37 K		38 M	39 P	40 T
41 U	42 V	43 E	44 J	45 S	46 Y	47 C	48 D	49 F		50 B	51 E	52 J		53 L	54 O
	55 X	56 Y	57 M		58 Q	59 S		60 U	61 F	62 D	63 I	64 K	65 N	66 O	67 Q
	68 S	69 T	70 V		71 W	72 Y		73 Y	74 A	75 B	76 E	77 J	78 T		79 A
80 D		81 C	82 F	83 P	84 S		85 Y	86 A	87 B		88 L	89 R	90 S	91 Y
92 Y	93 F		94 H	95 I	96 L		97 M	98 E		99 C	100 Q	101 R		102 X	103 C
104 F		105 G	106 O		107 T	108 U	109 V	110 W	111 E	112 H		113 I	114 S	115 T
116 A	117 J	118 R		119 R	120 T	121 C	122 Q	123 Y	124 V	125 W	126 A	127 U		128 F	129 I
130 M		131 A	132 B	133 V	134 T	135 O		136 A	137 J	138 L	139 N	140 P	141 R		142 S
143 T		144 D	145 E	146 I	147 Y	148 X	149 G	150 K	151 U	152 P	153 O		154 A	155 B	156 Y
157 S	158 N		159 Q	160 C	161 T	162 B		163 C	164 T	165 U	166 R		167 Q	168 H	169 R
	170 X	171 F	172 B	173 S	174 D	175 C	176 P		177 L	178 A		179 H	180 W	181 V	182 B
183 Q		184 F	185 Y	186 T	187 V	188 R	189 D	190 J		191 X	192 Y	193 E	194 N	195 M

The Naval Treaty

67. Here are some wide-open spaces from the longest short story in the Canon for you to fill in. Remember, starting boxes are listed on the last answer page.

ACROSS

1 "She gave a quick _____ of assent" (463)
4 Garden worker
5 Short sleep
8 "You are the stormy _____ of crime, Watson" (448)
10 Appellation
11 Exist
12 Soaked
14 "A rat could not conceal himself. . . . There is no _____ at all" (452)
15 The litmus-paper turned this color. (448)
16 "I knew well that Holmes loved his _____" (448)
18 Napoleon's isle, and others
19 502, to Messalina
20 Characteristic of Russell, Walton and Miken
21 Hair ointment
23 _____ Mineo
25 Pacino's
26 ". . . our kinship makes it the more impossible for me to _____ him in any way." (459)
28 Imitated
29 ". . . he was as ever ready to bring his _____ as his client could be to receive it" (448)
31 Sir Patrick _____, of ballad fame
32 Women's 1776 group, for short
33 Megacorporation, for short
36 Jewel measurement
37 _____ Ballou: film
39 Road material
40 Frenzied movement, usually with "run"
41 See 5 Down
43 Franklin, for one
44 French pronoun
45 Espionage agent

DOWN

1. Took down, or well known
2 Poetic contraction
3 Sketched
4 "_____ and now"
5 With 41 Across, a very important document
6 Singer Ed _____
7 _____ diem
8 Usually three, four or five
9 Command or pencil part
10 Watson thought Lord Holdhurst may have been truly this
13 The _____ Alliance (450)
14 Dresses; bedecks
17 Uncle: Span.
18 Common Latin abbreviation
22 ". . . before we reached home I was practically a raving _____" (454)
23 "But don't let yourself be drawn away upon a false _____" (452)
24 Suffixes for drunk or lagg
26 Do a keynote job
27 Cockney's tête
28 She wore one to attend to Phelp's ring (451)
30 Slang interjection
31 Identical
33 5 Down/41 Across was between England and _____ (450)
34 The _____ Gallery, London
35 Make an attempt
36 Taxi
38 Very: Fr.
42 Cockney's cry for assistance

68. Three more series of nonsense Anagrams for you to ponder. First a few of the people from our tale.

1. Any ruts, Meg?	(3,7)
2. Prey, C? ps Help!	(5,6)
3. R! Real hog cots?	(7,5)
4. Rollo Thrush, D.D.	(4,9)
5. O! Rains are in N.H.	(5,8)
6. Jars His Poor Hen	(6,8)
7. G! Ur, um, uu . . . I been sod.	(8,7)
8. Wolv, Bantim, Draf: Zu	(5,3,8)

69. Now, some places.

1. Lay it	(5)
2. "I reply."	(6)
3. "R.U.R.?" "Yes!"	(6)
4. Geld Nan	(7)
5. Ol' Raw Toe	(8)
6. Rend Blah to U, R.M.N.	(14)
7. Kin are big war, Bro!	(9,6)
8. "Jan, chap! Lot 'u 'n' I c, M?"	(7,8)

70. And finally, a few things, with clues attached.

1. Mr. Bodeo	(7)
2. "Irv, fear Ben."	(5,5 — a malady)
3. Puma et L.S.: R.I.P.	(6,5 — a testing device)
4. Vary a talent	(5,6 — political)
5. "Nubs" Reuben, R.N.	(6,6 — lab object)
6. "If I go for fence"	(7,6 — political)
7. Price all at line	(6,8 — political)
8. Dagmar closed ruts	(10,6 — military)

The Final Problem

71. Three quick Quotations first, to recall the flavor of this splendid story.

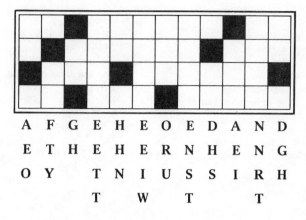

```
A   F   G   E   H   E   O   E   D   A   N   D
E   T   H   E   H   E   R   N   H   E   N   G
O   Y       T   N   I   U   S   S   I   R   H
        T       W   T           T
```

72. A metaphor later applied to Holmes himself.

```
D   E   E   O   F   I   I   K   E   E   A   C   B   N   I
L   E   R   S   I   L   I   S   H   M   O   E   E   O   N
R   E   S       S   N   T   T   S       W   T   I   P   T
H               T                       S
```

73. Watson's eulogy.

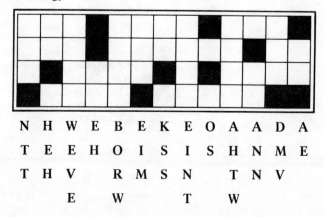

```
N   H   W   E   B   E   K   E   O   A   A   D   A
T   E   E   H   O   I   S   I   S   H   N   M   E
T   H   V       R   M   S   N       T   N   V
        E       W           T       W
```

74. A crossword "in memory of" the Master.

ACROSS

1 Occupations
5 Award statuette
10 Slightly open
14 Single entity
15 Actor Victor _____
16 Designer _____ Chanel
17 _____ Lisa, of Louvre fame
18 Set in earth: Var.
19 Weekday: Abbr.
20 "The Final _____" (469)
22 "... a pinnacle in the _____ of crime" (470)
24 Editor's concerns: Abbr.
25 Common verb ending
27 Sea eagle
28 1101, to Brutus
30 Trifle (with)
31 _____ Khan
34 "It was, _____, only too easy to do" (479)
36 The _____: old horror movie
37 Prefix for vision or scope
38 Nelson _____, singer
39 Choice food; delicacy: Arch.
40 MGM lion and others
41 Elizabeth II, for short
42 Confederate general
45 Some auto types, "initially"
46 Poetic contraction
49 Long thin fish
50 Poetic contraction
52 The hare, as it turned out
55 "... money is found for his bail or his _____" (471)
59 "_____ Comes the Bride"
60 Aqueous mammal
62 Shade of blue; freshwater duck
63 "_____ There" World War I song
64 "When I have _____ that I may cease to be": Keats
65 "He is the organizer of half that is _____" (471)
66 Belonging to Cratchit's son
67 Got up
68 Actor _____ Auberjonois

DOWN

1 "Into this hansom you will _____, and you will drive" (474)
2 "Where were you _____ about the evening of": Lawyerspeak, 2 wds.
3 Moriarty's celebrated treatise: 2 wds. (470)
4 Knife thrusts
5 New York theatre award
6 "... I should feel that my own career had reached its _____" (470)
7 Corn leftover
8 In medicine, lack of strength
9 Went on horseback
10 Olivier, for one
11 It ran an account of Holmes's "death": 3 wds.
12 Scored a quick point in tennis
13 Man's name
21 _____ M.F.T.: initials from an old ad campaign
23 Cerium: Abbr.
26 Negative
28 "Might I trouble you for a _____?" (470)
29 Net
32 Waiting for _____: Beckett
33 "The torrent ... plunges into a tremendous _____" (478)
35 Observe
36 Barbara _____ Geddes, actress
42 "... we saw a Swiss lad come running along ... with a _____ in his hand" (478)
43 _____ cummings
44 Steiler and Mycroft, for two
47 Large water pitchers
48 Scale note
50 The ace _____ spades
51 _____ Steiler, landlord (477)
52 "... we were rapidly gathering momentum, and an instant later had _____ clear of the station" (475)
53 Noted denim man
54 Living room piece
56 Irish Gaelic
57 The first fratricide
58 French pronoun
61 "The Way of _____"

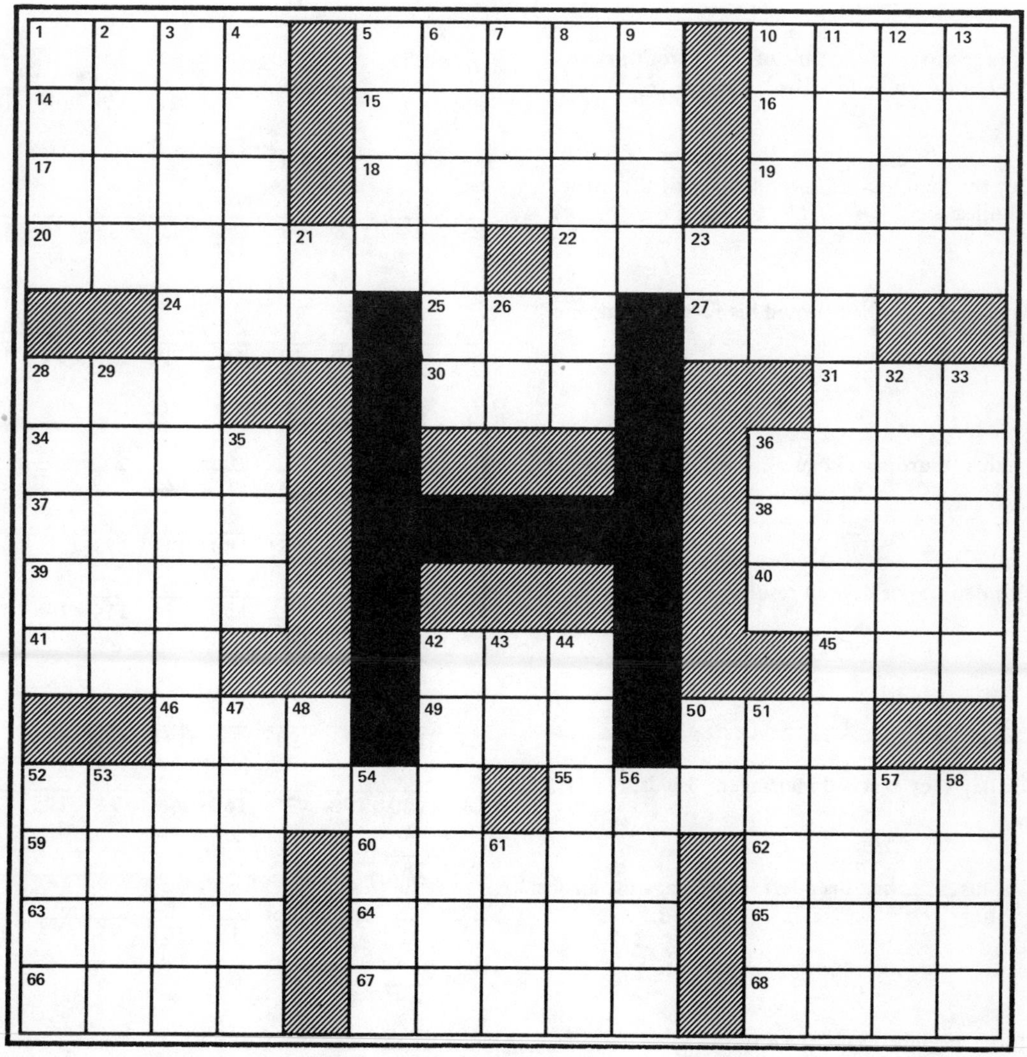
1 2 3 4 5 6 7 8 9 10 11 12 13
14 15 16
17 18 19
20 21 22 23
24 25 26 27
28 29 30 31 32 33
34 35 36
37 38
39 40
41 42 43 44 45
46 47 48 49 50 51
52 53 54 55 56 57 58
59 60 61 62
63 64 65
66 67 68

75. There won't be a dry eye in the house.

Clues

A "... the most brilliant bit of ____ work in the history of detection": 3 wds., Hyph. (471). . . . . .

<u>122</u> <u>51</u> <u>64</u> <u>111</u> <u>94</u> <u>128</u> <u>57</u> <u>163</u> <u>160</u>

<u>31</u> <u>148</u> <u>87</u> <u>101</u> <u>8</u>

B "But the man had ____ tendencies of the most diabolical kind" (470) . . . .

<u>85</u> <u>24</u> <u>118</u> <u>65</u> <u>177</u> <u>98</u> <u>133</u> <u>9</u> <u>156</u>

<u>16</u>

C "The aged ____ had turned his face towards me" (475) . . . .

<u>86</u> <u>17</u> <u>169</u> <u>32</u> <u>66</u> <u>99</u> <u>123</u> <u>52</u> <u>161</u>

<u>119</u> <u>149</u> <u>137</u>

D It had a "European vogue": 2 wds. (470). . . . . . .

<u>58</u> <u>157</u> <u>150</u> <u>18</u> <u>1</u> <u>125</u> <u>129</u> <u>53</u> <u>187</u>

<u>113</u> <u>33</u> <u>95</u> <u>180</u> <u>88</u> <u>153</u>

E With definite or desired results. . . . .

<u>158</u> <u>81</u> <u>89</u> <u>102</u> <u>130</u> <u>124</u> <u>114</u> <u>145</u> <u>168</u>

<u>54</u> <u>73</u>

F Uneasy rider? . . . .

<u>67</u> <u>151</u> <u>2</u> <u>10</u> <u>34</u> <u>134</u> <u>179</u> <u>154</u>

G The day they reached Meiringen: 3 wds. (477) . . .

<u>183</u> <u>120</u> <u>170</u> <u>3</u> <u>164</u> <u>68</u> <u>74</u> <u>175</u> <u>11</u>

<u>189</u>

H "... his ____ had been left leaning against a rock": Hyph. (479) . . . .

<u>121</u> <u>59</u> <u>167</u> <u>4</u> <u>19</u> <u>107</u> <u>35</u> <u>84</u> <u>131</u>

<u>69</u> <u>44</u>

I Florence Nightingale, for one. . . . .

<u>25</u> <u>82</u> <u>75</u> <u>166</u> <u>36</u>

J Moriarty met his at Reichenbach . . . .

<u>37</u> <u>60</u> <u>5</u> <u>108</u> <u>138</u>

K "____ the Bumblebee": 3 wds. . . . .

<u>38</u> <u>109</u> <u>178</u> <u>90</u> <u>142</u> <u>12</u> <u>143</u> <u>135</u> <u>45</u>

<u>76</u> <u>96</u>

L ____ McDaniel, of *GWTW* fame. . . . .

<u>46</u> <u>182</u> <u>13</u> <u>61</u> <u>70</u> <u>91</u>

M Noun, cousin to Letter E . . . .

<u>71</u> <u>115</u> <u>155</u> <u>136</u> <u>26</u> <u>47</u> <u>92</u> <u>174</u>

N Court . . . .

<u>139</u> <u>39</u> <u>62</u>

O Michievously . . . .

<u>140</u> <u>77</u> <u>100</u> <u>144</u> <u>14</u> <u>97</u> <u>172</u> <u>176</u>

P Perspiration, to vulgarians. . . . .

<u>103</u> <u>181</u> <u>27</u> <u>78</u> <u>40</u>

Q Current _____ . . . .
$\overline{104}\ \overline{20}\ \overline{146}\ \overline{79}\ \overline{48}\ \overline{126}$

R _____ *generis:* one of a kind . . . .
$\overline{132}\ \overline{191}\ \overline{28}$

S Massenet work . . . .
$\overline{93}\ \overline{41}\ \overline{29}\ \overline{49}\ \overline{184}$

T "The van dashed round by _____ Lane and was gone in an instant" (473) . . . .
$\overline{15}\ \overline{127}\ \overline{6}\ \overline{80}\ \overline{173}\ \overline{21}\ \overline{55}\ \overline{110}\ \overline{105}$
$\overline{116}$

U ". . . I had at last met an _____ who was my intellectual equal" (471) . . . .
$\overline{117}\ \overline{22}\ \overline{7}\ \overline{171}\ \overline{112}\ \overline{185}\ \overline{159}\ \overline{42}\ \overline{50}$
$\overline{72}$

V And so farewell to Moriarty, the _____: 3 wds. (471) . . . .
$\overline{43}\ \overline{162}\ \overline{147}\ \overline{152}\ \overline{141}\ \overline{56}\ \overline{188}\ \overline{186}\ \overline{190}$
$\overline{63}\ \overline{106}\ \overline{83}\ \overline{23}\ \overline{30}\ \overline{165}$

1 D	2 F	3 G	4 H	5 J	6 T	7 U	8 A		9 B	10 F	11 G	12 K	13 L	14 O
15 T	16 B		17 C	18 D	19 H	20 Q	21 T	22 U	23 V	24 B	25 I	26 M	27 P		28 R
	29 S	30 V		31 A	32 C	33 D	34 F	35 H	36 I	37 J		38 K	39 N		40 P
41 S	42 U	43 V	44 H		45 K	46 L	47 M	48 Q		49 S		50 U	51 A	52 C	53 D
54 E		55 T	56 V		57 A	58 D	59 H	60 J		61 L	62 N		63 V	64 A	65 B
66 C		67 F	68 G	69 H	70 L	71 M	72 U	73 E		74 G	75 I	76 K	77 O		78 P
79 Q	80 T		81 E	82 I	83 V	84 H	85 B	86 C	87 A		88 D	89 E	90 K	91 L	92 M
93 S	94 A		95 D	96 K		97 O	98 B	99 C		100 O	101 A	102 E	103 P	104 Q	105 T
106 V	107 H		108 J	109 K	110 T	111 A	112 U	113 D		114 E		115 M	116 T	117 U	118 B
	119 C	120 G	121 H	122 A		123 C	124 E		125 D	126 Q		127 T	128 A		129 D
	130 E	131 H	132 R	133 B		134 F	135 K	136 M	137 C	138 J		139 N	140 O	141 V	142 K
	143 K	144 O	145 E	146 Q		147 V	148 A	149 C	150 D		151 F	152 V		153 D	154 F
	155 M	156 B	157 D	158 E	159 U	160 A	161 C		162 V	163 A	164 G		165 V	166 I	167 H
168 E	169 C	170 G	171 U	172 O	173 T	174 M		175 G	176 O		177 B	178 K	179 F	180 D
	181 P	182 L	183 G	184 S	185 U	186 V		187 D	188 V		189 G	190 V	191 R	

The Adventure of the Empty House

76. Drum rolls and clashing cymbals—he's back in Baker Street!

ACROSS

1 1101, to Horace
4 Give up, as with land
8 Hello: Span.
9 Butter substitute
10 *Take the Money and _____:* Woody Allen film
11 25 Across played for these (484)
13 College degrees
14 "_____ in one"
15 Ms. Cannon's
18 Bit of leftover food
19 One piece of fruit: 2 wds.
21 Nipple
23 H feared W might betray this (488)
25 He was "Honourable," and all London was interested by his murder: Full name (483)
29 W's "affectionate _____" for H is what would have led him to betray H's 23 Across.
30 ". . . he passed rapidly . . . through a network of _____ and stables" (489)
33 Popular Indian transportation
34 Chinese New Year
35 Frequent road name in small towns: 2 wds., one abbr.
37 'Laugh-In" comedian _____ Johnson
38 Monosodium glutamate, for short
39 "To you . . . belongs the credit of the remarkable _____ which you have effected" (493)
41 "On thin _____"
42 H spent "some days with the head _____" (488)
43 Container
44 "_____ We Forget"
45 Carney or Garfunkel

DOWN

1 "The second most dangerous man in London" (494)
2 The Cavendish and the Bagatelle, for two
3 Mr. Fleming's
4 H researched the derivatives of this: Hyph. (488)
5 Ms. Sommers, actress and beauty
6 Scottish river
7 Dawn goddess
11 "No one had heard a _____" (484)
12 Ripped
15 Ten years
16 "Here he . . . passed through a wooden gate into a deserted _____" (489)
17 "The damp souls of housemaids/ Sprouting despondently at _____ gates": Eliot
19 Obliquely
20 Spanish name
22 High rocky hill
24 Cratchit progeny
26 Pet; body part
27 Khan and others
28 "From this convenient _____, the watchers were being watched" (490)
31 Soaks
32 Editor's notation
35 Meunier, of Grenoble (489)
36 ". . . the first criminal _____ in Europe." (483)
37 "_____ and the man I sing": Vergil
38 Crystallized, layered mineral
39 Everything
40 Female name

77. Considering the consequences, it won't be taken amiss if my Clue Line is read as an ironic comment on the Quotation. But still, it's good to have him back.

Clues

A "At the risk of telling a _____, I will recapitulate the facts": 3 wds. (483) . . . .

27 149 56 141 147 44 39 11 86

3 105 187 53

B ". . . I was well assured, from the bearing of this master _____, that the adventure was a most grave one" (488). . . . .

33 25 165 93 152 13 150 49

C "The crime was of interest in itself, but . . . was as nothing to me compared with the _____ sequel" (483) . . . .

81 75 172 17 64 104 71 114 84

154 186 30 137

D "Ronald Adair was fond of cards—playing occasionally, but never for such _____ as would hurt him" (484). . . . .

45 153 37 98 128 176

E Threatening; likely to happen without delay. . . . .

66 82 87 2 158 103 115 77

F "I have given you a serious _____ by my unnecessarily dramatic reappearance" (486) . . . .

148 102 60 19 142

G Jokingly: 2 wds. . . . .

157 127 24 8 78 180

H Nays, in elections: 2 wds. . . . .

134 94 9 59 124 188 72

I The Roman god of the lower world. . . . .

50 123 179

J "Yet it was upon this _____ young aristocrat that death came, in most strange and unexpected form": Hyph. (483). . . . .

112 167 151 16 159 174 73 122 166

K Adair's fiancée (483) . . . .

121 67 133 168 4

L "Ashes to ashes and _____": 3 wds. . . . .

116 18 160 110 74 83 156 12 26

184

M Plaster's partner . . . .

95 171 101 120

N ". . . that sudden flood of joy, amazement, and _____ which utterly submerged my mind" (483) . .

29 40 47 138 14 182 21 145 79

57 88

O "The Khalifa of _____" (488). . . . .

61 89 99 173 32 20 63 146

P ". . . that _____ five minutes on the Reichenbach ledge" (495). . . . .

90 7 162 58

Q One of "the poor bibliophile's" books: 3 wds. (485)

41 136 85 143 10 54 68 119 91

80

R Wit. . . . .
$\overline{113}$ $\overline{181}$ $\overline{169}$ $\overline{96}$ $\overline{126}$

S Made an intelligent guess. . . . .
$\overline{109}$ $\overline{51}$ $\overline{65}$ $\overline{6}$ $\overline{161}$ $\overline{185}$ $\overline{100}$ $\overline{46}$ $\overline{92}$

T The Earl _____: 2 wds. (483) . . . .
$\overline{97}$ $\overline{55}$ $\overline{177}$ $\overline{132}$ $\overline{183}$ $\overline{108}$ $\overline{76}$ $\overline{48}$ $\overline{35}$
$\overline{42}$

U ". . . a positive prohibition from his own _____"
(483) . . . .
$\overline{22}$ $\overline{107}$ $\overline{38}$ $\overline{135}$

V Persistent: tenacious . . . .
$\overline{23}$ $\overline{144}$ $\overline{131}$ $\overline{36}$ $\overline{118}$ $\overline{69}$

W Removes, as one's hat. . . . .
$\overline{129}$ $\overline{140}$ $\overline{5}$ $\overline{28}$ $\overline{175}$

X "Merridew of _____ memory" (494) . . . .
$\overline{34}$ $\overline{106}$ $\overline{70}$ $\overline{117}$ $\overline{164}$ $\overline{155}$ $\overline{43}$ $\overline{111}$ $\overline{31}$
$\overline{170}$

Y Small sailboat. . . . .
$\overline{178}$ $\overline{130}$ $\overline{1}$ $\overline{163}$

Z Melting snow . . . .
$\overline{15}$ $\overline{139}$ $\overline{125}$ $\overline{62}$ $\overline{52}$

1 Y	2 E	3 A	4 K		5 W	6 S	7 P	8 G		9 H	10 Q	11 A	12 L
13 B	14 N	15 Z		16 J	17 C	18 L		19 F	20 O	21 N	22 U	23 V		24 G	25 B
26 L	27 A		28 W	29 N	30 C	31 X		32 O	33 B	34 X	35 T		36 V	37 D	38 U
	39 A	40 N		41 Q	42 T	43 X	44 A		45 D	46 S	47 N	48 T	49 B	50 I	
51 S	52 Z	53 A	54 Q	55 T		56 A	57 N		58 P	59 H	60 F	61 O	62 Z		63 O
64 C	65 S	66 E	67 K	68 Q		69 V	70 X	71 C	72 H		73 J	74 L		75 C	76 T
77 E		78 G	79 N	80 Q		81 C		82 E	83 L	84 C	85 Q	86 A		87 E	88 N
	89 O	90 P	91 Q	92 S		93 3	94 H		95 M	96 R	97 T	98 D		99 O	100 S
	101 M	102 F	103 E		104 C	105 A	106 X	107 U	108 T	109 S	110 L		111 X	112 J	113 R
114 C	115 E	116 L		117 X	118 V		119 Q	120 M	121 K	122 J		123 I		124 H	125 Z
126 R	127 G	128 D	129 W		130 Y	131 V	132 T	133 K	134 H		135 U	136 Q	137 C	138 N	139 Z
140 W	141 A	142 F		143 Q	144 V	145 N	146 O	147 A	148 F		149 A	150 B	151 J		152 B
153 D	154 C	155 X	156 L	157 G	158 E	159 J		160 L	161 S	162 P	163 Y	164 X	165 B	166 J	
167 J	168 K		169 R	170 X		171 M	172 C	173 O	174 J	175 W	176 D		177 T	178 Y	
	179 I	180 G	181 R	182 N	183 T		184 L	185 S	186 C	187 A	188 H			

The Adventure of the Norwood Builder

78. The crux of our tale, in a single Hidden Phrase below.

```
H   A   E   H   T   U   T   E   S   L   I   N
R   E   A   N   D   E   N   I   M   A   X   E
S   L   Y   O   G   T   Y   O   E   T   N   H
L   Y   E   S   T   E   R   D   A   Y   S   W
X   D   L   B   X   I   W   T   K   I   F   E
A   C   M   A   R   K   A   Z   A   E   R   O
C   A   T   A   E   N   S   I   J   E   K   R
D   V   A   E   D   O   O   P   H   O   N   R
U   W   H   H   U   W   K   T   U   G   E   I
M   A   T   A   H   T   F   I   J   Q   V   H
```

1-4-4-4-4-3-3-5-4-1-8-3-4-9.

79. Below find every last name mentioned in our story, cryptically encoded.

1. WFSOFS

2. NPSJBSUZ

3. XBUTPO

4. NVSJMMP

5. PMEBDSF

6. NDGBSMBOF

7. HSBIBN

8. IPMNFT

9. DPSOFMJVT

10. TUFWFOT

11. MFYJOHUPO

12. IZBNT

13. MFTUSBEF

80. Don't be too terrified by this Super-Scramblegram. After you've read the story, the forty-three words below won't sound like such a mess but will recall memories of our tale. Rearrange them into a single sentence from our story. I have retained the original punctuation throughout.

WHEN HOLMES, HEARD A STORY OF SHOCKING CRUELTY
    TO A CAT HE WAS SO HORRIFIED THAT I HAD ENGAGED
    HIM, TO HAVE MR. AVIARY, TURNED
HIS HOW WAS LOOSE IN AN AND
BRUTAL HIM. MORE AT NOTHING WOULD DO WITH
I I I

The Adventure of the Dancing Men

81. To celebrate the second great code story in the Canon, here are five more Codes to ponder, starting with one that should look familiar.

82.

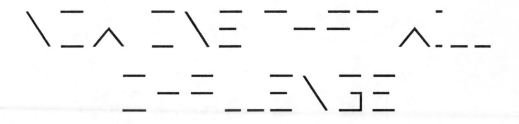

83. I CAN'T DISSOLVE THAT SOLUTION:
    BECAUSE DIDN'T A ROOSTER CIRCLE A WALKED!

84. Mayakovsky Bang Yermolov Borodin Bang Bang Tschaikovsky Humperdinck Bang Bang Bang Stanislavsky Bang Bang Bang Bang Nabokov Bang Bang Stanislavsky Turgenev Bang Bang Bang Bang Bang Bang Bang Bang Bang Bang Bang Stanislavsky Yermolov.

85. 1. Movement, as in "_____ pictures"   __ __ __ __ __ __ __
     2. Prepared; set   __ __ __ __ __ __
     3. Right; proper   __ __ __ __ __ __ __
     4. Nonlife   __ __ __ __ __ __
     5. Easy   __ __ __ __ __ __
     6. The _____ degree   __ __ __
     7. God's home   __ __ __ __ __ __
     8. Holiday, in America   __ __ __ __ __ __ __ __
     9. Peruvian camel   __ __ __ __ __
    10. Sight organs   __ __ __ __

The Adventure of the Solitary Cyclist

86. A few observations on human relations . . .

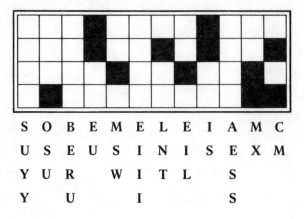

S	O	B	E	M	E	L	E	I	A	M	C
U	S	E	U	S	I	N	I	S	E	X	M
Y	U	R		W	I	T	L		S		
Y		U			I				S		

86. . . . on "getting the gist" . . .

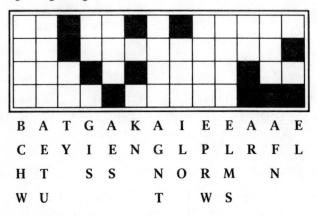

B	A	T	G	A	K	A	I	E	E	A	A	E
C	E	Y	I	E	N	G	L	P	L	R	F	L
H	T		S	S		N	O	R	M		N	
W	U				T		W	S				

88. . . . and the force of a fist.

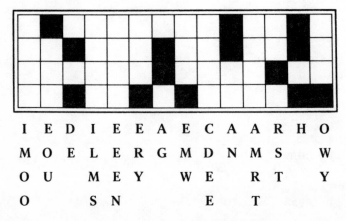

I	E	D	I	E	E	A	E	C	A	A	R	H	O
M	O	E	L	E	R	G	M	D	N	M	S		W
O	U		M	E	Y		W	E		R	T		Y
O			S	N			E		T				

The Adventure of the Priory School

89. A couple of Hidden Phrases for you, hidden, we hope, even better than Heidegger's body.

```
A M O A N T B E Y Z E A O L U Y
U E P H U T M Y S E L F F X I I
P L J V E G D X I T I F M V I W
T A D K S R N J W G I H A O M G
H A Q T E F A O I N F G Y I N O
T T P B C A S W S E E V C I D B
Z R R C E A B N A T U E T X H J
S Y X O E W I V E U A S T A S E
V B E Q N H N O T E E W V D H C
W O E L S R T O H R S E E H H T
P O I T P N A O E M N L K E J K
U D H T I I N T G A I T I R N S
G F S R E S N S I D N C L M H B
L T E H T I I D H O U N D S G A
X X C S T J J L K T Y T L Z E A
R E O T I W A O V H U F E Z V N
S M N E Q R O T W A L B U H F U
U K D R E S C E N T E Q D M P Z
Y B O A P H L O M I N I N L O O
Q J D S E I T I P S N I N H O H
E P E R H A P S K S O O F H G C
C E D R P C A O B Q L I T S O A
```

1. 7-3-5-2-3-2-4-3-4-3-3-6-4-6-3-6-3-3-1-5-2-2
2. 2-2-3-6-4-11-6-4-1-4-4-2-3-5

The Adventure of Black Peter

90. This and the other Word Detection puzzles found later in the book are collaborations between Mr. White and myself. He did the hard part—fitting in the longer words—and I added several entries to each and a Mystery Quotation from the leftover letters.

Allardyce's
Argentine

Black Peter
Brambletye Hotel

Cabin
Canadian Pacific
Canary
Captain Basil
Cardinal Tosca
Costa Rica

Deck
Dinghy

East End
Eggs

Forest Row
Fury

Ghost

Harpoon
Hugh Pattins
Hut

Key
Kit

Lancaster

Neligan
North
Norway

Path
Patrick Cairns
Peter Carey
Pig
Pipe
Puritan

Rope

San Paulo
Saxon
Sealer
Sea Unicorn
Shetland Lights
Slater
Spear
Stain
Stanley Hopkins
Stocks
Sumner
Sussex

Vicar

Wages
Watch
Wilson
Wit's
Woodman's Lee

Yacht
Yarn
Yell

```
A R G E N T I N E S P E A R S X I
L C H A I R O P E T E R C A R E Y
L I O K M T P U R I T A N C E S S
A F S T A N L E Y H O P K I N S E
R I T A H E T R E L A E S V M U A
D C P C B S A B U U P P K I U S U
Y A A L A N O S L I W I C W S A N
C P N C A B I O H A R P O O N D I
E N N C S D I A Y A C H T R O N C
S A S A X O N N T E Y K S T R E O
L I O S L A T E R P L U P S T T R
A D S T H G I L D N A L T E H S N
R A T I S N R I A C K C I R T A P
Y N U W E P I G E N R A Y O A E Y
H A H U G H P A T T I N S F P E R
G C W A G E S N T T H D E C K E U
N M A R S S T C O S T A R I C A F
I L E T O H E Y T E L B M A R B E
D E E L S N A M D O O W A T C H R
```

Mystery Quotation: __ ___ ____ _____

____ ____ ____ ____ _____.

91. Remorse isn't this one's long suit in our first Semi-Crostic.

Definitions	Words

Definitions

Neligan was murdered 2 days from these: 2 wds. (570)

Carey's bed (561)

". . . three parts drunk and in a _____ temper" (570)

He slew Peter

". . . I say I _____ Peter Carey (570)

Cairns had crewed this

Neligan lost his; H restored it

Words

26 39 22 17 6 12 41 9

23 1 32 21 20 43

10 29 41 14

34 3 7 18

15 24 38 19 5 13 42

4 33 11 30 16 31

25 27 40 30 8 19

2 19 35 37 9 28 36

Solution:

1 2 3 4 5 6 7 8 9 10 11 12 13 14

15 16 17 18 19 , 20 21 22 23 24 25 26 27 28 29 30 31

32 33 34 35 36 37 38 39 40 41 42 43 .

92. A Holmesian maxim.

Definitions

Wilson was this (561)

". . . the _____ of exercise before breakfast" (559)

H had high hopes for him: Full name (560)

The murder weapon (561)

". . . pinned like a _____ on a card" (561)

The impenetrable "_____" (564)

Neligan may have sued for this arrest

Words

2 18 39 25 36 28 21 7 4

41 10 33 7 35

26 34 13 37 8 31 14

5 6 24 19 40 2 15

5 23 22 24 1 17 37

29 3 35 39 11 31

12 42 32 16 9

20 38 30 27 3

Solution:

1 2 3 4 5 6 7 8 9 10 11 12 13 14 15 16 17 18 19

20 21 22 23 24 25 26 27 28 29 30 31

32 33 34 35 36 37 38 39 40 41 42

The Adventure of Charles Augustus Milverton

93. A heartwarming exchange.

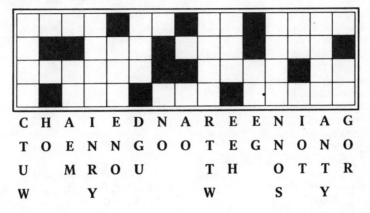

C H A I E D N A R E E N I A G
T O E N N G O O T E G N O N O
U _ M R O U _ _ T H _ O T T R
W _ Y _ _ _ _ _ W _ _ S _ Y

94. Ah, that Holmesian cool.

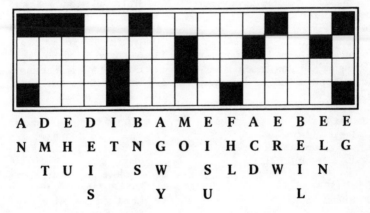

A D E D I B A M E F A E B E E
N M H E T N G O I H C R E L G
_ T U I _ S W _ S L D W I N _
_ _ S _ _ Y _ U _ _ _ L _ _ _

95. A strong contender for my favorite quotation in all of the Canon. And it's *all* here for you to puzzle over. Hints: It's a single quotation (quotation marks deleted), and the first and last squares are *not* blanks.

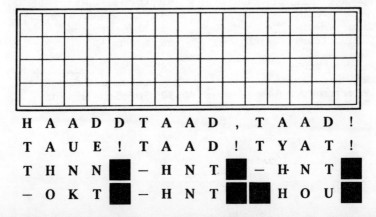

H A A D D T A A D , T A A D !
T A U E ! T A A D ! T Y A T !
T H N N ■ – H N T ■ – H N T ■
– O K T ■ – H N T ■ ■ H O U ■

96. This delightful tale (with the longest title in the Canon) fairly overflows with blackmail, burglary and murder. Here's a puzzle dedicated to the man who made it all possible.

ACROSS

1 The Lady's (573)
5 A bust of her was in Milverton's study (578)
11 It was thick and warm in the conservatory (577)
14 Apparently, he wouldn't have understood (573)
15 Lovable monkey, popular with vivisectionists
16 Actress _____ Merkel (friend to puzzle makers)
17 A big fire or a little fire
18 1002, to Ovid
19 Flashback to the "Pips" terror group: Abbr.
20 Nunnery bigwig
22 Dry: Fr.
25 2, to Seneca
26 Work on a manuscript
27 ". . . we had become _____ in the eyes of the law." (577)
29 Dorothy's dog
33 Quieting sound
34 Exclamation or a *bête noir* for a foreigner's spelling lesson
35 What W never did to his word (576)
37 Mr. Wiesel's
41 Observe
42 Moving less fast
45 Drivers' group: Abbr.
48 Awake, watchful: Ital.
49 "'Then you are not _____,' said I" (576)
51 Reverberation
54 Amon _____, Egyptian idol
56 ". . . the ruffian, who in hot blood bludgeons his _____" (573)
57 Earlier; quicker
60 Unexpected difficulty
63 _____ Post, cereal magnate, "initially"
64 Poetic "before"
65 Appledore _____ (572)
68 Sculling necessity
70 Mamma or Farrow
71 "_____ Camera": 3 wds.
74 Three: Ital.
75 Alternating prayer
78 Betelgeuse or Betty Grable
79 Theater personnel: Abbr.
80 They had a "rich, choking fragrance" (578)
81 Something to do with Christmas or bees

DOWN

1 ☓ ☓ ☓
2 Large cask
3 Wild buffalo of India
4 Large, flat rock
5 Milverton warned H that he was this (575)
6 "_____ Your Life": old TV show, 2 wds.
7 "_____ in London," said H to W, re Milverton: 5 wds. (572)
8 Exist: Span.
9 Greek letter
10 It: Ger.
11 Northern diving bird
12 Comic book production stage
13 Holmesian disguise: the "_____ young workman" (575)
21 Exist
22 Asimov's genre, for short
23 _____ cummings
24 *Huis _____ (No Exit)*: Sartre play
28 "I love my wife, but _____ kid," "alphabetically"
29 Lung diseases: Abbr.
30 Smelting material
31 "_____ the line"; keep your nose clean
32 All right: Sl.
36 Suffix for Japan or Pekin
38 Chinese mile
39 The "_____ crowd"
40 Ovum: Eng.
43 Linnaean Society: Abbr.
44 Bible section: Abbr.
45 Architect's group: Abbr.
46 Pismire
47 The _____ of Reason
48 " 'You've _____ me,' he cried, and lay still" (581)
50 Sacred Hindu mantra

51 H's temporary *nom de guerre* (576)
52 "... your _____ heart cannot keep your lips from twitching" (580)
53 One of Santa's sounds
55 Consecrate, with oil
58 Comparative ending
59 Concerning: Lat.
61 Lengthy distance, as in "We still have _____ to go": Sl., 2 wds.

62 Where "Progress is our Most Important Product": Abbr.
66 "I have only to consider the question of personal _____" (576)
67 Fill; satisfy
69 "*In medias* _____"
72 West
73 Type of music synthesizer
75 Record type: Abbr.
76 French pronoun
77 Scottish article

The Adventure of the Six Napoleans

97. There's a 25-word Hidden Phrase below, fairly bursting out at you, so—just this once—I've deleted the letter counts.

```
I  L  A  R  E  A  S  O  N  I  N  G
W  T  N  E  P  R  N  S  I  H  O  M
A  T  B  O  A  N  T  H  H  H  D  A
S  B  X  T  D  N  H  R  U  Q  E  C
U  M  T  R  E  I  A  O  M  R  Y  H
C  K  I  M  S  N  T  F  A  C  A  I
H  W  O  E  A  S  D  G  N  M  R  N
E  M  E  H  E  T  K  L  O  L  T  E
N  A  S  O  C  A  F  O  B  T  E  A
B  E  T  N  E  N  E  V  T  I  B  N
V  O  Y  A  H  T  J  E  K  P  V  D
M  A  N  S  L  T  R  S  F  O  R  U
M  O  N  O  I  T  A  R  I  M  D  A
E  L  E  D  U  I  M  T  E  L  E  U
P  Z  N  B  A  P  P  L  A  U  S  E
```

98. The Scramblegram below, which badly requires rearranging, nevertheless retains its proper punctuation.

IF YOU USE WATSON, THE ONLY VALUABLE PRESS, TO KNOW A INSTITUTION, HOW MOST IS IT.

99. Here are seven owners of the Napoleons, and seven partial addresses. Each group has its own code. After solving the names, test your memory by matching the partial address to the owner.

Owners
(Hint: Two letters equal themselves in this one.)

Addresses
(Hint: Y=P; P=Y)

1. GIBJIV MZJ KY.

2. AYVUI FSJUYZ

3. JV. LMVZEKYT

4. FYVMKI FMVCIV

5. FMVJEZG LVYTFIVU

6. DYUEMF LVYQZ

7. AV. UMZJIHYVJ

A. DJAAFAHUZA WZNK

B. GFHG VUWJJU

C. VUJYAJP

D. CZRJW MWFQUZA WZNK

E. DJAVFAHUZA

F. WJNKFAH

G. LGFVRFLD

The Adventure of the Three Students

100. These three quotations sum up all the knowledge Holmes required to solve his case.

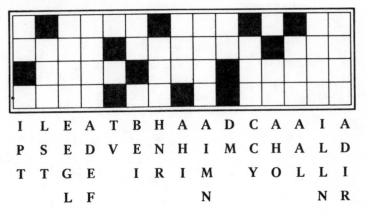

```
I  L  E  A  T  B  H  A  A  D  C  A  A  I  A
P  S  E  D  V  E  N  H  I  M  C  H  A  L  D
T  T  G  E     I  R  I  M     Y  O  L  L  I
   L  F           N              N  R
```

101.

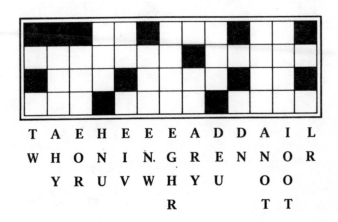

```
T  A  E  H  E  E  E  A  D  D  A  I  L
W  H  O  N  I  N  G  R  E  N  N  O  R
   Y  R  U  V  W  H  Y  U     O  O
                  R        T  T
```

102.

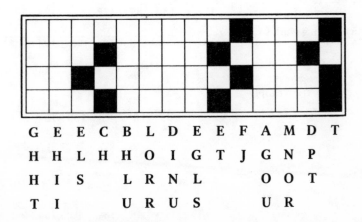

```
G  E  E  C  B  L  D  E  E  F  A  M  D  T
H  H  L  H  H  O  I  G  T  J  G  N  P
H  I  S     L  R  N  L     O  O  T
T  I        U  R  U  S     U  R
```

The Adventure of the Golden Pince-Nez

103. This was the first Holmes story I ever read, and it's still one of my favorites, partly because of the Quotation you are about to see materialize before your very eyes.

Clue

A H said glasses provided a fine field for _____ (612) .

 $\overline{42}$ $\overline{34}$ $\overline{66}$ $\overline{15}$ $\overline{79}$ $\overline{156}$ $\overline{21}$ $\overline{50}$ $\overline{174}$

B Well-known London gallery. . . . .

 $\overline{44}$ $\overline{181}$ $\overline{72}$ $\overline{105}$

C The victim: Full name (609) . . . .

 $\overline{76}$ $\overline{58}$ $\overline{64}$ $\overline{131}$ $\overline{22}$ $\overline{167}$ $\overline{119}$ $\overline{45}$ $\overline{68}$

 $\overline{9}$ $\overline{11}$ $\overline{28}$ $\overline{159}$ $\overline{51}$ $\overline{145}$

D *Jaws* town . . . .

 $\overline{188}$ $\overline{86}$ $\overline{52}$ $\overline{12}$ $\overline{177}$

E "_____ Days"; youth . . . .

 $\overline{106}$ $\overline{4}$ $\overline{163}$ $\overline{141}$ $\overline{24}$

F Confused; in a quandary . . . .

 $\overline{165}$ $\overline{29}$ $\overline{120}$ $\overline{151}$

G Where Coram kept the bureau key: Hyph. (614) . .

 $\overline{82}$ $\overline{161}$ $\overline{144}$ $\overline{53}$ $\overline{122}$ $\overline{186}$ $\overline{192}$ $\overline{134}$ $\overline{65}$

 $\overline{16}$

H "Holmes gave an ejaculation of _____" (611). . . . .

 $\overline{73}$ $\overline{107}$ $\overline{124}$ $\overline{1}$ $\overline{170}$ $\overline{157}$ $\overline{164}$ $\overline{43}$ $\overline{148}$

 $\overline{180}$

I Rent. . . . .

 $\overline{74}$ $\overline{153}$ $\overline{54}$ $\overline{121}$ $\overline{193}$

J Bambi, for one . . . .

 $\overline{93}$ $\overline{67}$ $\overline{190}$ $\overline{25}$

K Popular Japanese import. . . . .

 $\overline{17}$ $\overline{35}$ $\overline{87}$ $\overline{196}$ $\overline{155}$ $\overline{83}$

L "He can give no _____ of the young man's last words" (610) . . . .

 $\overline{46}$ $\overline{38}$ $\overline{182}$ $\overline{55}$ $\overline{108}$ $\overline{59}$ $\overline{129}$ $\overline{36}$ $\overline{3}$

 $\overline{171}$ $\overline{118}$

M The housekeeper: 2 wds. (609) . . . .

 $\overline{132}$ $\overline{89}$ $\overline{172}$ $\overline{5}$ $\overline{123}$ $\overline{147}$ $\overline{112}$ $\overline{37}$ $\overline{84}$

N The object of H's deciphering work (607) . . . . . .

 $\overline{39}$ $\overline{18}$ $\overline{75}$ $\overline{90}$ $\overline{194}$ $\overline{47}$ $\overline{160}$ $\overline{26}$ $\overline{166}$

 $\overline{94}$

O ". . . I have to arrange for a fresh supply _____": 2 wds. (615). . . . .

 $\overline{85}$ $\overline{100}$ $\overline{91}$ $\overline{168}$ $\overline{109}$ $\overline{23}$ $\overline{6}$ $\overline{48}$ $\overline{56}$

 $\overline{135}$ $\overline{149}$ $\overline{60}$ $\overline{95}$ $\overline{158}$

P Navy builder. . . . .

 $\overline{61}$ $\overline{113}$ $\overline{27}$ $\overline{127}$ $\overline{77}$ $\overline{101}$

Q The maid (609). . . . .

 $\overline{110}$ $\overline{49}$ $\overline{184}$ $\overline{40}$ $\overline{154}$ $\overline{62}$ $\overline{7}$

R Where Letter C spent his boyhood (609) . . . . $\overline{69}$ $\overline{162}$ $\overline{183}$ $\overline{30}$ $\overline{92}$ $\overline{102}$ $\overline{2}$ $\overline{96}$ $\overline{19}$

S "____ upon a time" . . . . $\overline{178}$ $\overline{142}$ $\overline{31}$ $\overline{133}$

T Official decree . . . . $\overline{13}$ $\overline{139}$ $\overline{103}$ $\overline{114}$ $\overline{185}$

U Hopkins (608) . . . . $\overline{136}$ $\overline{97}$ $\overline{41}$ $\overline{179}$ $\overline{8}$ $\overline{80}$ $\overline{128}$

V Geographical designation: 2 wds. . . . . $\overline{176}$ $\overline{125}$ $\overline{32}$ $\overline{152}$ $\overline{173}$ $\overline{20}$ $\overline{195}$ $\overline{137}$

W Stagehands' union: Abbr. . . . . $\overline{187}$ $\overline{111}$ $\overline{115}$ $\overline{126}$ $\overline{140}$

X It was about a hundred yards from the house:
2 wds. (611) . . . . $\overline{104}$ $\overline{81}$ $\overline{116}$ $\overline{14}$ $\overline{169}$ $\overline{33}$ $\overline{150}$ $\overline{138}$ $\overline{189}$

$\overline{146}$

Y "____ is better than none": 3 wds. . . . . $\overline{57}$ $\overline{117}$ $\overline{98}$ $\overline{88}$ $\overline{10}$ $\overline{130}$ $\overline{143}$ $\overline{175}$ $\overline{63}$

Z What Letter Y often turns into . . . . $\overline{70}$ $\overline{99}$ $\overline{78}$ $\overline{71}$ $\overline{191}$

1 H	2 R		3 L		4 E	5 M		6 O	7 Q	8 U	9 C
	10 Y		11 C	12 D	13 T	14 X	15 A	16 G	17 K		18 N	
19 R	20 V	21 A		22 C	23 O		24 E	25 J	26 N	27 P	28 C	29 F		30 R
31 S	32 V	33 X	34 A	35 K	36 L		37 M	38 L	39 N	40 Q	41 U	42 A	43 H	
44 B	45 C	46 L		47 N	48 O	49 Q	50 A	51 C	52 D	53 G	54 I	55 L		56 O	57 Y
58 C	59 L	60 O	61 P		62 Q	63 Y		64 C	65 G	66 A	67 J		68 C	69 R	70 Z
	71 Z	72 B	73 H	74 I	75 N		76 C	77 P		78 Z	79 A	80 U		81 X	82 G
83 K	84 M	85 O		86 D	87 K		88 Y	89 M	90 N	91 O	92 R	93 J		94 N	95 O
96 R	97 U		98 Y	99 Z	100 O	101 P		102 R	103 T	104 X	105 B	106 E		107 H	108 L
109 O		110 Q	111 W	112 M	113 P		114 T	115 W	116 X	117 Y	118 L	119 C	120 F		121 I
122 G	123 M	124 H	125 V	126 W		127 P	128 U		129 L	130 Y	131 C		132 M	133 S	134 G
135 O	136 U		137 V	138 X	139 T	140 W		141 E	142 S	143 Y	144 G	145 C	146 X	147 M
148 H	149 O	150 X	151 F	152 V	153 I	154 Q	155 K	156 A		157 H	158 O		159 C	160 N
161 G		162 R	163 E	164 H	165 F	166 N	167 C	168 O	169 X		170 H	171 L		172 M	173 V
	174 A		175 Y	176 V	177 D	178 S	179 U	180 H		181 B	182 L	183 R	184 Q	185 T
	186 G	187 W	188 D	189 X	190 J		191 Z	192 G	193 I	194 N		195 V	196 K

The Adventure of the Missing Three-Quarter

104. Uncle Mount-James the miser.

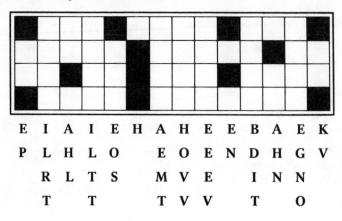

```
E  I  A  I  E  H  A  H  E  E  B  A  E  K
P  L  H  L  O     E  O  E  N  D  H  G  V
R  L  T  S     M  V  E     I  N  N
T     T     T  V  V     T     O
```

105. One of the greatest conceits in the Canon.

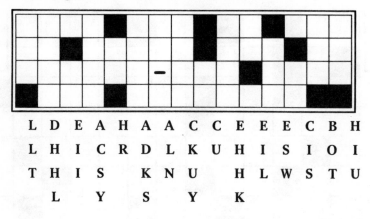

```
L  D  E  A  H  A  A  C  C  E  E  E  C  B  H
L  H  I  C  R  D  L  K  U  H  I  S  I  O  I
T  H  I  S     K  N  U     H  L  W  S  T  U
L     Y     S     Y     K
```

106. Another Holmesian swipe at our long-suffering chronicler.

```
D  O  H  A  D  D  A  F  L  E  A  D  I  D  C
R  O  H  O  E  G  E  L  P  E  C  F  N  O  N
Y  T  S  R  U  R  H  M  R  R  M  I  O  U  N
   U  S              Y     O  T  Y
```

The Adventure of the Abbey Grange

107. Jury Duty at Baker Street (see the Mystery Quotation).

Abbey Grange
Adelaide
Art (highest entry only)
Australia

Bass Rock
Beeswing
Bell
Body
Book
Brackenstall

Cab
Captain Crocker
Coat
Cool
Cord

Elms

Glass
Gown

Habit
Hatpin
Hopkins
Hot

Kent

Lady
Lewisham Gang
Liar

Maid
Marengo

Mary Fraser
Murdered

New York

Palladio
Poker

Randalls
Rock of Gibraltar

Sir Eustace
Suez Canal
Sydenham

Theresa Wright

Waterloo

```
D R N K R O Y W E N D O T R A
I A D A C T K G U E I I L I Y
A T I R P O K E R C B T L B D
M L C O O L R E T A W A T R A
A A Y B M C D S H P R O R A L
R R H S I R E U S T A C E C E
E B A N U A T Y S A B B S K W
N I T M E N Y U A I B E A E I
G G P L E D A O L N E E R N S
O F I K O A Y S G C Y S F S H
W O N B R L M S D R G W Y T A
N K P A L L A D I O R I R A M
S C A B E S U E Z C A N A L G
H O P K I N S A I K N G M L A
O R A D E L A I D E G D I E N
T H G I R W A S E R E H T B G
```

"Mystery Quotation: "_ _ _ _ _ _ _ _ _,

_ _ _ _ _ _ _," _ _ _ _ _.

108. "Elementary, my dear Watson" are the four most famous words Holmes never uttered (in that order, at any rate). In our first Quotation, you'll find the four most famous ones that he did. (That's why I'm making you work for them.)

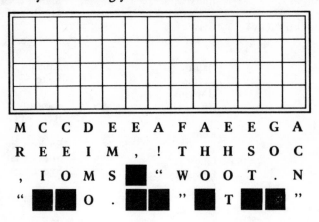

```
M  C  C  D  E  E  A  F  A  E  E  G  A
R  E  E  I  M  ,  !  T  H  H  S  O  C
,  I  O  M  S  ■  "  W  O  O  T  .  N
"  ■  ■  O  .  ■  ■  "  ■  T  ■  ■  "
```

109. A lover's apologia.

```
L  E  A  S  E  C  A  D  L  A  I  F
T  H  E  V  P  M  H  E  M  D  N  I
T  H  I  W     O  O  E  R     O  N
H  O           W  U  R
```

110. And the cymbal crash that ties in all the others, including our Mystery Quotation in Puzzle 107.

```
P  A  A  E  I  I  C  O  E  C  A  C  A
V  O  C  I  N  O  P  R  L  D  K  E  E
X  T  D  Q  P     T  T  O  I     R  O
      X     U     Y  U  U        V  R
```

The Adventure of the Second Stain

111. Sorry about all these Quotations all of a sudden. I ran into the same problem I had with puzzle #24. However, I'm not so sorry for these as I was for those others. These are all wonderfully late Victorian and British. But then, I've always been a sucker for a "Come, sir!" when it's smartly barked.

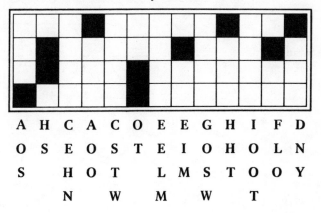

```
A H C A C O E E G H I F D
O S E O S T E I O H O L N
S   H O T   L M S T O O Y
    N   W   M   W     T
```

112. It's on its way.

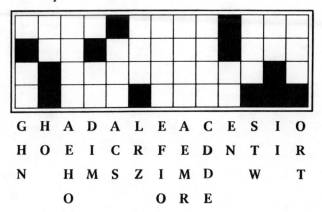

```
G H A D A L E A C E S I O
H O E I C R F E D N T I R
N   H M S Z I M D   W   T
    O       O R E
```

113. Here it is.

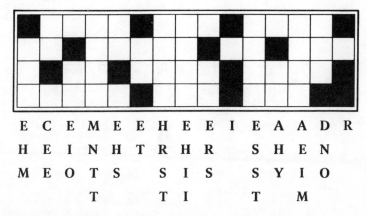

```
E C E M E E H E E I E A A D R
H E I N H T R H R   S H E   N
M E O T S   S I S   S Y I   O
    T       T I     T   M
```

114. I wish he'd treated them more like Windibank.

Clues

A His career was suddenly placed in jeopardy:
Full name (650) . . . .
$\overline{35}$ $\overline{92}$ $\overline{24}$ $\overline{68}$ $\overline{71}$ $\overline{8}$ $\overline{116}$ $\overline{101}$ $\overline{1}$

$\overline{130}$ $\overline{32}$ $\overline{86}$ $\overline{184}$

B Member of a South African group. . . . .
$\overline{160}$ $\overline{74}$ $\overline{28}$ $\overline{165}$ $\overline{102}$ $\overline{53}$ $\overline{187}$ $\overline{146}$ $\overline{135}$

C One of H's chief attributes . . . .
$\overline{44}$ $\overline{80}$ $\overline{174}$ $\overline{49}$ $\overline{121}$ $\overline{105}$

D American humorist . . . .
$\overline{18}$ $\overline{59}$ $\overline{152}$ $\overline{47}$ $\overline{117}$

E Letter X was "an _____ gossip" (658) . . . .
$\overline{62}$ $\overline{128}$ $\overline{41}$ $\overline{137}$ $\overline{11}$ $\overline{4}$ $\overline{109}$ $\overline{131}$ $\overline{94}$

$\overline{56}$ $\overline{177}$ $\overline{82}$ $\overline{190}$

F Where H can presently be found, tending his bees:
2 wds: (650) . . . .
$\overline{162}$ $\overline{20}$ $\overline{38}$ $\overline{132}$ $\overline{178}$ $\overline{99}$ $\overline{141}$ $\overline{118}$ $\overline{171}$

$\overline{156}$ $\overline{182}$

G In accord: 3 wds. . . . .
$\overline{77}$ $\overline{119}$ $\overline{9}$ $\overline{150}$ $\overline{166}$ $\overline{172}$ $\overline{161}$ $\overline{129}$ $\overline{29}$

H Folk singer's get-together . . . .
$\overline{110}$ $\overline{157}$ $\overline{185}$ $\overline{159}$ $\overline{6}$ $\overline{140}$ $\overline{134}$ $\overline{143}$ $\overline{147}$

$\overline{50}$

I Be ready for; expect . . . .
$\overline{139}$ $\overline{52}$ $\overline{179}$ $\overline{91}$ $\overline{12}$

J Pension: Fr. . . . .
$\overline{95}$ $\overline{170}$ $\overline{25}$ $\overline{148}$ $\overline{43}$

K ". . . the _____ in question is of such immense
importance" (651) . . . .
$\overline{46}$ $\overline{70}$ $\overline{114}$ $\overline{85}$ $\overline{15}$ $\overline{98}$ $\overline{164}$ $\overline{97}$

L To H, this was the giveaway . . . .
$\overline{17}$ $\overline{136}$ $\overline{67}$ $\overline{163}$ $\overline{34}$

M Seaman's call . . . .
$\overline{64}$ $\overline{120}$ $\overline{155}$ $\overline{37}$

N "_____ places me in a very delicate position":
2 wds. (656) . . . .
$\overline{124}$ $\overline{73}$ $\overline{3}$ $\overline{5}$ $\overline{58}$ $\overline{115}$ $\overline{103}$ $\overline{61}$ $\overline{21}$

$\overline{63}$ $\overline{188}$ $\overline{123}$

O Request . . . .
$\overline{40}$ $\overline{88}$ $\overline{65}$ $\overline{104}$ $\overline{7}$ $\overline{142}$ $\overline{183}$ $\overline{149}$ $\overline{173}$

$\overline{78}$

P Absolutely not: Sl., 2 wds. . . . .
$\overline{48}$ $\overline{125}$ $\overline{180}$ $\overline{111}$ $\overline{108}$

Q Site of famous altarpiece . . . .
$\overline{106}$ $\overline{13}$ $\overline{90}$ $\overline{45}$ $\overline{153}$

R Little one's word for parent . . . .
$\overline{55}$ $\overline{16}$ $\overline{76}$ $\overline{89}$ $\overline{144}$

S Jazz refrain . . . .
$\overline{138}$ $\overline{26}$ $\overline{158}$ $\overline{186}$

T Celestial phenomenon associated with Letter D:
2 wds. . . . .
$\overline{42}$ $\overline{81}$ $\overline{107}$ $\overline{175}$ $\overline{30}$ $\overline{22}$ $\overline{69}$ $\overline{145}$ $\overline{10}$

$\overline{189}$ $\overline{96}$ $\overline{112}$

U New York theatre award. . . . .
$\overline{87}$ $\overline{19}$ $\overline{154}$ $\overline{66}$

V Term of endearment . . . .
$\overline{83}$ $\overline{51}$ $\overline{168}$ $\overline{14}$ $\overline{79}$

W Ape . . . .
$\overline{23}$ $\overline{113}$ $\overline{133}$ $\overline{169}$ $\overline{31}$

X Henri Fournaye, to some: Full name (654). . . . . .
$\overline{93}$ $\overline{176}$ $\overline{126}$ $\overline{39}$ $\overline{167}$ $\overline{75}$ $\overline{2}$ $\overline{122}$ $\overline{151}$

$\overline{100}$ $\overline{60}$ $\overline{54}$

Y Watson's favorite word. . . . .
$\overline{84}$ $\overline{127}$ $\overline{27}$ $\overline{72}$ $\overline{33}$ $\overline{57}$ $\overline{181}$ $\overline{36}$

1 A	2 X	3 N		4 E	5 N	6 H		7 O	8 A	9 G		10 T	11 E		12 I
13 Q	14 V			15 K	16 R	17 L	18 D		19 U	20 F	21 N	22 T		23 W	24 A	25 J
	26 S	27 Y		28 B	29 G	30 T		31 W	32 A	33 Y	34 L	35 A	36 Y	37 M	
38 F	39 X	40 O	41 E		42 T	43 J		44 C	45 Q	46 K		47 D	48 P		49 C
50 H		51 V	52 I	53 B		54 X	55 R	56 E	57 Y	58 N		59 D	60 X	61 N	
62 E		63 N	64 M	65 O	66 U		67 L	68 A	69 T	70 K		71 A		72 Y	73 N
74 B	75 X		76 R	77 W	78 O	79 V		80 C	81 T	82 E	83 V	84 Y		85 K	86 A
87 U	88 O		89 R	90 Q		91 I		92 A	93 X	94 E	95 J	96 T	97 K		98 K
99 F	100 X	101 A	102 B	103 N	104 O	105 C	106 Q	107 T	108 P		109 E	110 H	111 P	112 T
113 W		114 K	115 N	116 A	117 D	118 F	119 G		120 M	121 C	122 X	123 N		124 N	125 P
126 X		127 Y	128 E		129 G	130 A	131 E	132 F		133 W	134 H	135 B	136 L	137 E	138 S
	139 I	140 H	141 F		142 O	143 H	144 R		145 T	146 B	147 H	148 J	149 O	150 G	151 X
152 D	153 Q	154 U	155 M	156 F		157 H	158 S		159 H	160 B	161 G	162 F		163 L	164 K
165 B	166 G	167 X	168 V	169 W	170 J	171 F		172 G	173 O	174 C	175 T	176 X		177 E	178 F
	179 I		180 P	181 Y	182 F	183 O	184 A		185 H	186 S		187 B	188 N	189 T	190 E

The Hound of the Baskervilles

115. Watson on his own, in the longest and, in some ways, most satisfying of all the Holmes tales. If we cannot dedicate the Hound puzzles to Watson's acuity, we can to his fidelity, perseverance and, above all, his grace of style, as both the Clue Line and Quotation will illustrate.

Clues

A The motive for murder . . . .
204 39 158 56 17 77 128 1 135
80 59

B The means: 3 wds. (675) . . . .
190 38 90 83 115 40 122 68 105
108 187

C "Author of 'Some Freaks of ____' (*Lancet*, 1882)" (671) . . . .
71 93 132 4 168 102 192

D What all is, as the Preacher saith . . . .
18 193 96 37 189 62

E "The ____": eighteenth-century philosophical movement . . . .
86 156 183 19 79 175 36 111 203
140 179 54 157

F Sir Hugo and Stapleton, for instance . . . .
116 74 167 52 5 210 25 173 20
150 114 180

G Napoleon's isle . . . .
26 124 125 209

H Irritable: Sl. . . . .
191 42 206 188

I Stapleton's "cover" . . . .
144 35 164 119 10 151 21 53 110
2

J Where Laura Lyons lived: 2 wds. (751) . . . .
160 95 65 34 12 131 127 6 202
174 141 207

K Funeral ceremony . . . .
99 64 88 43 89 162 7

L Wicked . . . .
205 27 126 46 199 98 166

M The last of Letter F: 2 wds. (685) . . . .
87 101 178 172 22 163 186 104

N What gave Watson away: Var. (740) . . . .
182 121 23 33 165 137 67

O "She has fainted from ____ and exhaustion": Comp. (758) . . . .
134 32 61 82 92 24 55 208

P Rodgers and Hammerstein musical . . . .
181 76 44 13 146 138 70 107

Q Harshly . . . .
153 11 195 45 78 73 148 152

R Stapleton's former trade . . . .
$\overline{14}$ $\overline{31}$ $\overline{47}$ $\overline{147}$ $\overline{161}$ $\overline{85}$ $\overline{113}$ $\overline{118}$ $\overline{106}$
$\overline{8}$ $\overline{184}$ $\overline{194}$

S Board, come, going, or side . . . .
$\overline{155}$ $\overline{123}$ $\overline{198}$

T One of the two "moorland farmhouses" (684) . . .
$\overline{41}$ $\overline{177}$ $\overline{66}$ $\overline{49}$ $\overline{130}$ $\overline{94}$ $\overline{60}$ $\overline{200}$

U Dawdler, laggard: Sl. . . . .
$\overline{97}$ $\overline{142}$ $\overline{50}$ $\overline{201}$ $\overline{154}$ $\overline{81}$ $\overline{15}$ $\overline{159}$

V Geometrical figure. . . . .
$\overline{100}$ $\overline{3}$ $\overline{30}$ $\overline{143}$ $\overline{58}$ $\overline{196}$ $\overline{72}$

W March maneuver: 2 wds. . . . .
$\overline{57}$ $\overline{176}$ $\overline{129}$ $\overline{9}$ $\overline{48}$ $\overline{139}$ $\overline{185}$ $\overline{145}$ $\overline{170}$

X Editing; cutting. . . . .
$\overline{169}$ $\overline{16}$ $\overline{109}$ $\overline{112}$ $\overline{120}$ $\overline{69}$ $\overline{28}$ $\overline{136}$

Y Clumsy one . . . .
$\overline{51}$ $\overline{63}$ $\overline{197}$

Z New _____, town in Nabokov's *Pale Fire* . . . .
$\overline{171}$ $\overline{149}$ $\overline{91}$

Z_1 Sofa-chair often found in the Canon . . . .
$\overline{75}$ $\overline{29}$ $\overline{84}$ $\overline{133}$ $\overline{103}$ $\overline{117}$

1 A	2 I		3 V	4 C	5 F	6 J	7 K		8 R	9 W	10 I	11 Q	
12 J	13 P	14 R	15 U	16 X	17 A	18 D	19 E	20 F	21 I	22 M		23 N	24 O	25 F	26 G
	27 L	28 X		29 Z_1	30 V	31 R	32 O	33 N	34 J	35 I	36 E	37 D	38 B	39 A
40 B	41 T		42 H	43 K	44 P	45 Q	46 L	47 R	48 W		49 T	50 U	51 Y	52 F	53 I
54 E	55 O		56 A	57 W	58 V	59 A	60 T	61 O	62 D		63 Y	64 K	65 J	66 T	67 N
	68 B	69 X	70 P		71 C	72 V	73 Q		74 F	75 Z_1	76 P	77 A	78 Q	79 E
80 A	81 U	82 O	83 B	84 Z_1	85 R	86 E	87 M	88 K		89 K	90 B	91 Z	92 O	93 C	94 T
95 J	96 D	97 U		98 L	99 K		100 V	101 M	102 C		103 Z_1	104 M	105 B	106 R
107 P	108 B	109 X		110 I	111 E	112 X	113 R	114 F	115 B		116 F	117 Z_1	118 R	119 I	120 X
121 N	122 B	123 S	124 G		125 G	126 L	127 J		128 A	129 W		130 T	131 J		132 C
	133 Z_1	134 O	135 A	136 X	137 N		138 P	139 W		140 E	141 J	142 U	143 V	144 I	145 W
146 P	147 R	148 Q	149 Z		150 F	151 I	152 Q		153 Q	154 U	155 S	156 E		157 E	158 A
159 U		160 J	161 R	162 K	163 M	164 I	165 N	166 L	167 F	168 C	169 X	170 W		171 Z	172 M
173 F	174 J	175 E		176 W	177 T	178 M	179 E		180 F	181 P		182 N	183 E	184 R	185 W
186 M	187 B	188 H		189 D	190 B	191 H		192 C	193 D	194 R	195 Q		196 V	197 Y	
198 S	199 L	200 T		201 U	202 J	203 E	204 A	205 L	206 H		207 J	208 O	209 G	210 F

116. Here's a foggy crossword, as treacherous as the Grimpen Mire, for you to find your way through. Beware the rocks and wild beasts that lurk in the middle.

ACROSS

1 "It's in the _____"; all wrapped up
4 Russian oxcart
5 Southeast Asian country
6 "_____, Ho!": sailor's call
7 Where H hid on the moor (741)
10 Heat measurement: Abbr.
13 "... the settled _____ of Nature" (681)
15 Suffix for Japan or Pekin
16 Thailand, once
17 "_____ - high"
18 Comedian Steve _____
20 Expectant fathers are known to do this.
21 The _____ Office: Presidents' lair
22 "Learn ... not to fear the fruits of the _____" (674)
23 "Here are two moorland farmhouses, _____ and Foulmire": 2 wds. (684)
26 New York or London area
29 Aware of: Sl.
30 Oriental exclamation of understanding: 2 wds.
31 "There is a realm in which the most _____ ... of detectives is helpless" (680)
33 Cleopatra's serpent
36 Man's, woman's or a storm's name
37 _____ the Beachcomber
38 Golf course, or things that are missing
40 Self
41 "... his mind was prepared for just such an _____ as did eventually overtake him" (673)
42 Manner; way of carrying oneself
43 Two unconsecutive notes for the scale
44 Eddie _____, the French Connection detective
45 Lighting instrument accessory

DOWN

1 This was used to revive Sir Henry and Mrs. Stapleton (757)
2 "... a diabolical agency which makes Dartmoor an unsafe _____ for a Baskerville" (682)
3 Petrol, to Yanks
4 Do it for _____: on a whim: 2 wds.
6 Angeles
7 "... this dreadful apparition, exactly corresponding to the _____ of the legend": Hyph. (681)
8 Employ, often exploitatively
9 Christie's "_____ Little Indians"
10 "I will not _____ your mind by suggesting theories" (698)
11 Savoir faire; ability to deal with delicate situations
12 English philosopher, to a Cockney
14 _____ Shankar
16 Health resort
19 Hang back
21 Cousin to Aha!
22 For
24 Explosive
25 The 'ilton, or the 'oliday Hinn, for instance
26 "... ask him to send up a pound of the strongest _____ tobacco" (682)
27 Scandinavian capital
28 Garden implement
30 "The _____ of Reason"
31 American humorist, or a summer drink
32 Against
33 "There could be no doubt about the beetling forehead, the sunken _____ eyes" (745)
34 "... another thread which I have extricated out of the tangled _____" (720)
35 Abbreviation for person, poison or prison?
39 "He ... was the very _____, they tell me, of the family picture of old Hugo" (681)
43 Running limb

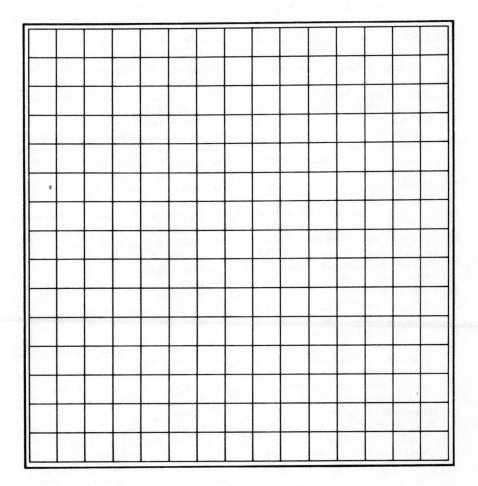

The Valley of Fear

117. Another romp through vicious America and back. Our secret society here was based on a real one—the Molly Maguires—that operated around eastern Pennsylvania in the coal-mining areas shortly after the Civil War.

ACROSS

1 "... the people concerned and the strange setting in which their fate was _____" (779)
5 George's lyricist brother
8 _____ - Magnon Man
11 Kettle: Span.
12 Moat shape
14 "What are you but the paid _____ of the capitalists" (831)
15 East Indian vine
16 Foolish; absurd
17 He: Lat.
18 "... face to face with an infinite possibility of _____ evil" (826)
20 "... read twelve hours a day at the _____ of crime" (777)
22 Teachers' organization: Abbr.
23 Child's game
24 Costs, as in a hotel
26 "Take to one's _____": flee
29 Wilbur, in Charlotte's Web
30 N.Y. gambling establishment
32 W.W. II area
33 Sandra, or a Scottish river
34 Place for 29 Across
35 Lighting instrument accessory
36 Pancake enhancer
40 Person or thing beyond hope: Sl.
43 Unwell
44 Chicken _____ king: 2 wds.
45 It burned on the study table (782)
48 "He was a silent, precise man with a dour _____" (773)
52 Lily plant
53 "He always went about _____" (793)
57 "... Moriarty rules with a rod of _____ over his people" (777)
58 Jail: Sl.
59 "The house ... was threatening to moulder into a picturesque _____" (780)
60 "... his gold chains more weighty across a more gorgeous _____" (826)
61 A hill, from our last story
62 Accomplished
63 Ogles

DOWN

1 Vermissa Valley industry
2 Summer and Smoke heroine
3 Thin opening
4 "... _____ instantly recognizes genius" (773)
5 Minute particle
6 Pit for roots: Maori
7 Woman's name
8 Carbonated beverage
9 Croissant, for one
10 Spanish cheers
12 Moreno and Gam
13 "There is only one punishment in his code. It is _____" (778)
14 "Without having a _____ of cruelty in his singular composition" (774)
19 Born
21 Mr. Mac's "no"
24 "... we have certain _____, and also certain duties of our own" (833)
25 "... I would read as easily as I do the apocrypha of the _____ column" (770)
27 "There's no town without a _____" (817)
28 Hereford, for one
29 Get-up-and-go
31 Actress Barbara _____ Geddes
37 "Though a wretched _____, he turned out at every meet" (780)
38 Norse god and expert bowman
39 Argue, as a law case
40 _____ dancer: Railway worker
41 Spanish greeting
42 "Your _____ shrewdness, my dear Watson, that innate cunning which is the delight of your friends" (770)
45 Dramatis personae
46 Vocal part
47 Le Rouge et le _____: Stendhal
49 American discoverer of heavy hydrogen
50 JFK's mother
51 Participial endings
54 "... a kind of sixth sense that waves the _____ flag" (813)
55 1101, to Livy
56 Cockney tête

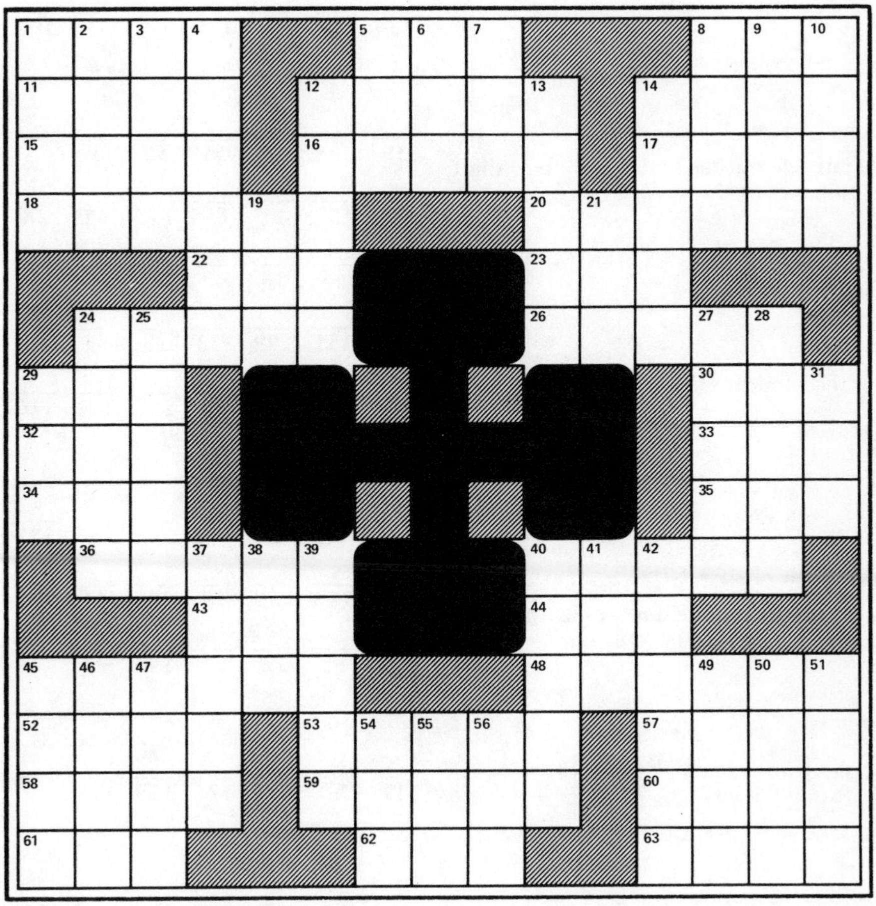
1 2 3 4 5 6 7 8 9 10
11 12 13 14
15 16 17
18 19 20 21
22 23
24 25 26 27 28
29 30 31
32 33
34 35
36 37 38 39 40 41 42
43 44
45 46 47 48 49 50 51
52 53 54 55 56 57
58 59 60
61 62 63

118. Another graceful Watsonian rumination, together with a portentous Clue Line.

Clues

A "First thoughts": 3 wds. (769) . . . .
$\overline{134}$ $\overline{25}$ $\overline{34}$ $\overline{156}$ $\overline{62}$ $\overline{79}$ $\overline{198}$ $\overline{175}$ $\overline{105}$

$\overline{4}$ $\overline{86}$

B Short marching paces: 2 wds. . . . .
$\overline{59}$ $\overline{168}$ $\overline{203}$ $\overline{65}$ $\overline{52}$ $\overline{1}$ $\overline{7}$ $\overline{185}$ $\overline{120}$

C "You've got us side-tracked with your interesting _____, Mr. Holmes" (777) . . . .
$\overline{92}$ $\overline{157}$ $\overline{13}$ $\overline{89}$ $\overline{141}$ $\overline{67}$ $\overline{28}$ $\overline{126}$ $\overline{204}$

D The Valley of Fear (811) . . . .
$\overline{191}$ $\overline{45}$ $\overline{38}$ $\overline{68}$ $\overline{136}$ $\overline{148}$ $\overline{173}$ $\overline{16}$

E Butler's Utopia . . . .
$\overline{69}$ $\overline{151}$ $\overline{199}$ $\overline{133}$ $\overline{98}$ $\overline{31}$ $\overline{46}$

F The one on the window sill and others (792) . . . .
$\overline{55}$ $\overline{19}$ $\overline{71}$ $\overline{80}$ $\overline{149}$ $\overline{161}$ $\overline{116}$ $\overline{123}$ $\overline{147}$

$\overline{187}$ $\overline{42}$

G Birdie (855) . . . .
$\overline{144}$ $\overline{33}$ $\overline{21}$ $\overline{150}$ $\overline{122}$ $\overline{166}$ $\overline{177}$

H Peanut oil, for one . . . .
$\overline{117}$ $\overline{112}$ $\overline{130}$ $\overline{49}$ $\overline{201}$ $\overline{44}$ $\overline{174}$

I "Porlock, Watson, is a _____, a mere identification mark": Comp., 3 wds. (769) . . . .
$\overline{131}$ $\overline{95}$ $\overline{72}$ $\overline{94}$ $\overline{190}$ $\overline{24}$ $\overline{140}$ $\overline{10}$ $\overline{100}$

$\overline{194}$

J ". . . it was just one _____ too late" (798) . . . .
$\overline{12}$ $\overline{88}$ $\overline{160}$ $\overline{176}$ $\overline{129}$ $\overline{115}$ $\overline{58}$

K Combining form meaning "the back" . . . .
$\overline{135}$ $\overline{40}$ $\overline{188}$ $\overline{64}$

L _____ Wells (803) . . . .
$\overline{27}$ $\overline{81}$ $\overline{124}$ $\overline{197}$ $\overline{3}$ $\overline{73}$ $\overline{63}$ $\overline{106}$ $\overline{30}$

M _____, Sweet Charlotte: Film, 2 wds. . . . .
$\overline{15}$ $\overline{41}$ $\overline{155}$ $\overline{113}$ $\overline{162}$ $\overline{184}$ $\overline{107}$ $\overline{167}$

N Immediately afterward: Arch. . . . .
$\overline{51}$ $\overline{109}$ $\overline{9}$ $\overline{91}$ $\overline{37}$ $\overline{182}$ $\overline{74}$ $\overline{159}$

O Promises; swears . . . .
$\overline{169}$ $\overline{108}$ $\overline{183}$ $\overline{119}$

P Presuming that: 2 wds. . . . .
$\overline{61}$ $\overline{178}$ $\overline{97}$ $\overline{128}$ $\overline{20}$ $\overline{48}$ $\overline{75}$ $\overline{146}$

Q "I believe that I am one of the most _____ of mortals": Comp. (769) . . . .
$\overline{165}$ $\overline{139}$ $\overline{82}$ $\overline{143}$ $\overline{76}$ $\overline{114}$ $\overline{18}$ $\overline{54}$ $\overline{101}$

$\overline{57}$ $\overline{50}$ $\overline{193}$ $\overline{125}$

R Often a waltz: 2 wds. . . . .
$\overline{32}$ $\overline{142}$ $\overline{138}$ $\overline{83}$ $\overline{23}$ $\overline{196}$ $\overline{93}$ $\overline{6}$ $\overline{102}$

S Numerical ending . . . .
$\overline{22}$ $\overline{103}$ $\overline{189}$

T Alcohol necessity . . . .
$\overline{85}$ $\overline{158}$ $\overline{180}$ $\overline{60}$ $\overline{137}$

U Hatfield/McCoy and Montague/Capulet: 2 wds. .
$\overline{163}$ $\overline{202}$ $\overline{17}$ $\overline{78}$ $\overline{170}$ $\overline{154}$ $\overline{181}$ $\overline{26}$

V "_____ Best": TV series, 2 wds. . . . .
$\overline{96}$ $\overline{172}$ $\overline{127}$ $\overline{39}$ $\overline{90}$ $\overline{84}$ $\overline{152}$ $\overline{36}$ $\overline{132}$
$\overline{200}$ $\overline{14}$

W Plume . . . .
$\overline{110}$ $\overline{99}$ $\overline{35}$ $\overline{145}$ $\overline{66}$ $\overline{192}$ $\overline{11}$

X Reverberation . . . .
$\overline{5}$ $\overline{70}$ $\overline{179}$ $\overline{53}$

Y Sneeze, onomatopoeically . . . .
$\overline{87}$ $\overline{2}$ $\overline{171}$ $\overline{29}$ $\overline{186}$ $\overline{111}$

Z ". . . the thought of _____ had become a remote one" (858) . . . .
$\overline{195}$ $\overline{43}$ $\overline{47}$ $\overline{118}$ $\overline{56}$ $\overline{153}$ $\overline{164}$ $\overline{121}$ $\overline{104}$
$\overline{77}$ $\overline{8}$

1 B	2 Y	3 L	4 A	5 X	■	6 R	7 B	8 Z	9 N	10 I	11 W	12 J	13 C	14 V	■
15 M	16 D	17 U	■	18 Q	19 F	20 P	21 G	22 S	23 R	■	24 I	25 A	26 U	27 L	
28 C	29 Y	30 L	■	31 E	32 R	33 G	■	34 A	35 W	36 V	37 N	38 D	■	39 V	40 K
41 M	42 F	43 Z	■	44 H	45 D	46 E	47 Z	48 P	49 H	50 Q	51 N	52 B	■	53 X	54 Q
■	55 F	56 Z	57 Q	58 J	59 B	60 T	■	61 P	62 A	63 L	■	64 K	65 B	■	66 W
67 C	68 D	69 E	70 X	71 F	72 I	73 L	74 N	75 P	76 Q	■	77 Z	78 U	■	79 A	80 F
81 L	82 Q	83 R	84 V	85 T	■	86 A	87 Y	88 J	89 C	90 V	91 N	■	92 C	93 R	94 I
■	95 I	96 V	■	97 P	98 E	99 W	■	100 I	101 Q	102 R	103 S	104 Z	105 A	106 L	107 M
■	108 O	109 N	■	110 W	111 Y	112 H	■	113 M	114 Q	115 J	116 F	117 H	118 Z	119 O	■
120 B	121 Z	122 G	123 F	124 L	125 Q	126 C	■	127 V	128 P	129 J	130 H	■	131 I	132 V	133 E
■	134 A	135 K	■	136 D	137 T	138 R	■	139 Q	140 I	141 C	■	142 R	143 Q	144 G	
145 W	146 P	147 F	148 D	■	149 F	150 G	151 E	152 V	■	153 Z	154 U	155 M	156 A	157 C	158 T
159 N	160 J	■	161 F	162 M	163 U	164 Z	165 Q	166 G	■	167 M	168 B	169 O	170 U	■	171 Y
172 V	173 D	174 H	■	175 A	176 J	177 G	■	178 P	179 X	180 T	181 U	182 N	183 O	■	184 M
■	185 B	186 Y	187 F	■	188 K	189 S	■	190 I	■	191 D	192 W	193 Q	194 I		
■	195 Z	196 R	197 L	198 A	199 E	■	200 V	201 H	202 U	203 B	204 C				

119. From another great code story comes this third round of cryptic messages to challenge you. Again the first one will look familiar, though I warn you the others may send you screaming into the night.

549 42/3 3/9 39/5 24/2

23/9 14/3 2/11 6/9 8/9 27/10

7/1 23/1 44/9.

38/5!

120.

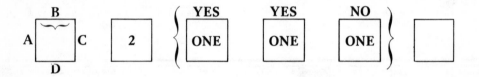

121. RTU BE WTSU MTO NNODNAB ASEDO CRO FSESUBE.

122. (Hint: Your struggle here will be squarely against time.)

DERÉS ERESI CEHMS ÈIPYT :ECNA

123.
117 94, (134 65 / 85 163 48 / 138 185 126 19 165 158 23 / 37 184 27 / "101 63," / 85 20 81' 49 144 / 182 74 / 9 98 30 / 21 122 80 187 106 / 130 151 16 79 152)

128 79 106: (26 90 99?) 51 169 / 15 108 32 69 / 92 183 191 199 22, 119 135? / 25 109 45 / 158 112 34 91 40 103 / 55 169 83 / 59 202 87 131 159 33 / 41 2 / 168 108 183 135.

(68 13)

124. Here's another of Mr. White's Monogram Mazes. This one has you caught right in the middle of five very tough characters, led by Bodymaster McGinty. While they're closing in, see how fast you can get out of the maze to safety, without passing through any of the enemies' space.

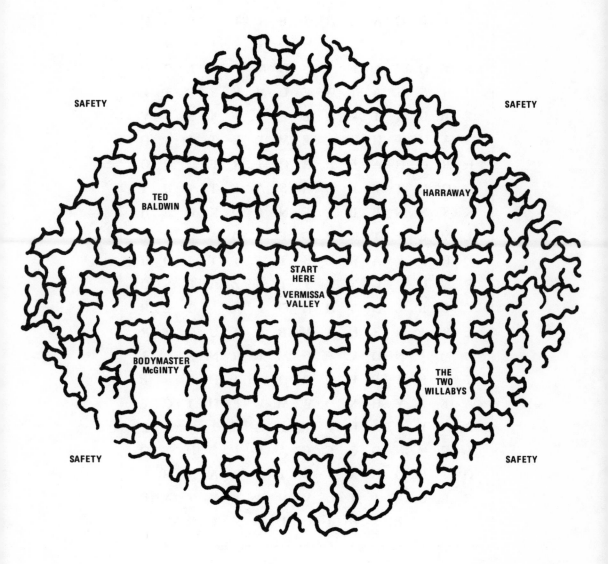

The Adventure of Wisteria Lodge

125. A couple of Hidden Phrases for you, both of which mirror the discomforting eccentricity of our tale.

```
T  A  B  G  A  H  H  S  B  I  T  I  S  G  M
H  C  D  E  F  G  T  H  O  I  R  J  K  R  L
E  M  O  N  E  F  I  O  D  M  P  Q  L  O  U
R  R  S  S  A  T  W  E  U  V  E  R  Y  T  L
E  M  U  S  T  V  E  E  R  W  X  S  E  Y
Z  A  H  I  H  R  L  E  M  B  E  T  C  S  D
H  R  O  H  A  E  P  R  O  I  R  F  H  Q  O
G  O  U  T  V  E  O  H  S  A  I  T  J  U  T
K  S  S  N  E  B  E  E  N  L  Q  K  W  E  H
L  M  E  I  T  N  P  G  E  E  O  A  P  U  E
Q  R  S  Y  A  W  E  S  T  A  T  T  J  Q  H
S  N  U  V  W  X  N  Y  I  S  Z  A  B  S  O
C  O  B  E  D  T  H  H  O  E  A  F  T  E  R
L  K  I  R  S  H  A  N  B  U  T  U  G  T  R
D  M  J  N  O  V  P  Q  M  E  R  N  S  O  I
I  E  S  T  E  P  F  R  O  M  T  H  E  R  B
A  E  Z  Y  H  X  Q  W  M  V  P  U  T  G  L
A  N  B  C  A  D  E  F  I  G  H  I  J  K  E
L  O  M  N  D  O  C  C  A  S  I  O  N  T  O
O  T  P  Q  E  R  E  H  T  K  R  A  M  E  R
R  C  U  P  I  T  U  V  N  W  X  Y  Z  A  B
B  D  F  B  S  H  J  O  L  M  N  P  R  S  X
```

1. 2-2-9-6-3-2-1-4-3-8-2-6-5-2-3-3-4-4-3-9-2-3-8.
2. 5-4-4-4-4-4-7-6-4-4-4-7-4-2-4-5.

The Adventure of the Cardboard Box

126. I couldn't resist deleting letter counts again on this 22-word Hidden Phrase (one of H's slickest thrusts at W). The starting letter, however, is "T."

```
A  L  M  Y  F  A  I  T  H  F  U  L
T  E  D  O  E  A  S  B  W  K  A  S
F  N  G  U  R  R  N  Y  H  O  W  E
A  H  F  R  A  T  A  D  I  E  L  R
S  U  T  S  E  H  E  E  C  S  E  V
N  N  H  O  S  T  M  T  H  E  N  A
O  F  E  A  T  U  R  E  S  T  S  N
I  I  N  V  M  A  N  A  A  I  H  T
T  R  J  K  I  E  C  R  E  M  A  S
O  E  O  H  B  G  E  D  E  U  L  R
M  V  I  S  S  E  R  P  X  E  L  Z
E  S  A  W  L  E  X  Y  K  A  Q  M
```

127. Try this Scramblegram once in your head.

of her wife's body in my soul. and of the whole footmark I did more than mud thought I

128. Holmes turns contemplative in many of these later tales.

```
I  H  A  I  E  I  B  E  D  C  B  E
W  O  F  S  M  O  C  E  E  C  L  Y
   S  H  T  S  R  S  I  R  Y  T
   T              V  J  R
```

129. The good old agony column. (Hint: R=M)

"IJFW RJ!" XFNI MJ, YZWSNSL TAJW YMJ UFLJX, "BMFY

F HMTWZX TK LWTFSX, HWNJX, FSI GQJFYNSLX! BMFY

F WFL-GFL TK XNSLZQFW MFUUJSNSLX."

130. In this cryptogram, Holmes's rules for the frequency of letter usage (as outlined in the "Dancing Men" tale) are strongly in evidence.

ONEMKDSYX XOFOB OXNC, GKDCYX. SD SC K COBSOC

YP VOCCYXC GSDR DRO QBOKDOCD PYB DRO VKCD.

131. Understatement time.

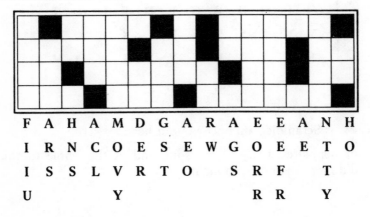

```
F A H A M D G A R A E E A N H
I R N C O E S E W G O E E T O
I S S L V R T O   S R F   T
U     Y           R R   Y
```

132. He probably did.

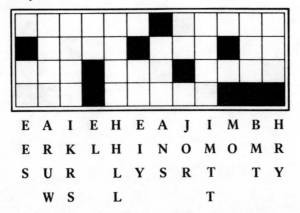

```
E A I E H E A J I M B H
E R K L H I N O M O M R
S U R   L Y S R T   T Y
W S   L       T
```

The Adventure of the Bruce-Partington Plans

133. A Word Detection puzzle with a vintage Holmesian Mystery Quotation.

Agony Column
Aldgate

Blood
Bruce-Partington

Cadogan West
Case
Charing Cross

Fog

Goldini

Hugo Oberstein

Jupiter

Key

Lassus
Lestrade

Mason
Meyer
Mycroft

Pierrot
Pipe
Points

Safe
Siam
Sidney Johnson

Sir James Walter
Spy
Submarine

Taps
Theatre
Theft
Track
Trams

Underground

Valentine Walter
Violet Westbury

Woolwich

```
T E S P Y I W E D A R T S E L B
E F U I P E L O R N F O G A R V
S A E N R Y K E O E T R H U E I
A S E H D J Y S N L E R C M T O
C G A U T E A I A T W E A M L L
H A E G M M R M A F P I O R A E
A T D O O A Y G E A S P C H W T
R T E O M N D C R S G G A H E W
I M H B G L Y T R O W J E S N E
N L U E A A I C L O U A T P I S
G S A R A N N D O P F N L A T T
C S B S G T I W I L I T D T N B
R O L T S N R T E O U P W R E U
O N O E I U E E P S S M E A L R
S N O I A R S M A R T K N C A Y
S I D N E Y J O H N S O N K V E
```

Mystery Quotation: __ __ __ __ __ __ __ __ __ __ __ __

__ __ __ __ __ __ __ __ __ __ __ __ __

__ __ __ __ __ __ __ __ __ .

The Adventure of the Dying Detective

134. "As I, perchance, hereafter shall think meet
To put an antic disposition on . . ."

Clues

A "Of all ruins, that of ____ is the most deplorable":
3 wds. (935) . . . .
<u> 9 </u> <u> 17 </u> <u> 32 </u> <u> 36 </u> <u> 52 </u> <u> 72 </u> <u>198</u> <u> 73 </u> <u> 99 </u>
<u>114</u>

B The villain: Full name . . . .
<u>177</u> <u>196</u> <u> 11 </u> <u>112</u> <u>132</u> <u>135</u> <u>156</u> <u>161</u> <u>193</u>
<u> 59 </u> <u> 12 </u> <u> 23 </u> <u> 48 </u> <u> 84 </u>

C Drama by *The Skin of Our Teeth* author: 2 wds. .
<u> 96 </u> <u>119</u> <u>123</u> <u>138</u> <u>144</u> <u> 4 </u> <u> 46 </u>

D Musical ____ *I Sing*: 2 wds. . . . .
<u> 81 </u> <u> 8 </u> <u> 38 </u> <u> 64 </u> <u> 77 </u> <u> 88 </u>

E Mrs. Hudson, to H . . . .
<u>128</u> <u>183</u> <u>200</u> <u> 22 </u> <u> 28 </u> <u> 43 </u> <u>100</u> <u>154</u>

F "It is ____ deadly, and it is horribly contagious"
(933) . . . .
<u>168</u> <u>179</u> <u> 25 </u> <u> 47 </u> <u> 65 </u> <u>129</u> <u>190</u> <u>142</u> <u>175</u>
<u>194</u>

G All . . . .
<u> 18 </u> <u>145</u> <u> 30 </u> <u> 41 </u> <u> 95 </u> <u>106</u> <u>116</u> <u>140</u>

H W's recommended specialist: 2 wds. . . . .
<u>201</u> <u> 21 </u> <u> 51 </u> <u> 57 </u> <u> 74 </u> <u> 94 </u> <u>104</u> <u>120</u> <u>143</u>
<u>146</u>

I "A sick man ____": 4 wds. (933) . . . .
<u>192</u> <u> 79 </u> <u>151</u> <u>174</u> <u>186</u> <u> 26 </u> <u> 63 </u> <u> 71 </u> <u>101</u>
<u>136</u> <u> 24 </u>

J Captain America or Wonder Woman . . . .
<u>105</u> <u>149</u> <u>121</u> <u>157</u> <u>166</u> <u>187</u> <u> 20 </u> <u> 44 </u> <u>115</u>

K Decathlon division . . . .
<u>171</u> <u>180</u> <u> 40 </u> <u> 54 </u> <u> 69 </u>

L Letter H: "the greatest living ____ on tropical
diseases" (934) . . . .
<u> 78 </u> <u> 97 </u> <u>124</u> <u>126</u> <u>134</u> <u>147</u> <u>199</u> <u> 7 </u> <u> 14 </u>

M Term of endearment . . . .
<u>125</u> <u>133</u> <u>181</u> <u> 53 </u> <u> 90 </u> <u> 1 </u>

N "Oh, Wilderness were Paradise ____!": Fitzgerald .
<u> 55 </u> <u>150</u> <u>153</u> <u> 60 </u>

O ". . . this magnificent intellect babbling like a
____": 2 wds. (936) . . . .
<u> 82 </u> <u>163</u> <u>165</u> <u>176</u> <u> 10 </u> <u>159</u> <u> 39 </u> <u> 75 </u> <u>110</u>
<u> 27 </u> <u>184</u> <u> 33 </u>

P Where Mrs. Hudson says H contracted his malady
(932) . . . .
<u> 87 </u> <u>173</u> <u>189</u> <u> 61 </u> <u> 85 </u> <u> 92 </u> <u>139</u> <u> 66 </u> <u>130</u>
<u>164</u> <u>109</u>

Q Basketball defense tactic: 3 wds. . . . .
$\overline{2}\ \overline{6}\ \overline{58}\ \overline{178}\ \overline{107}\ \overline{34}\ \overline{141}\ \overline{113}$

R "...his often _____ scientific experiments" (932).
$\overline{67}\ \overline{103}\ \overline{170}\ \overline{195}\ \overline{137}\ \overline{15}\ \overline{50}\ \overline{118}\ \overline{3}$
$\overline{155}$

S Ed Norton, for one . . . .
$\overline{191}\ \overline{13}\ \overline{102}\ \overline{45}\ \overline{76}\ \overline{29}\ \overline{98}\ \overline{160}$

T "Very smart of you to notice it, but rather _____ to suggest that it was cause and effect" (939) . . . .
$\overline{16}\ \overline{162}\ \overline{86}\ \overline{131}\ \overline{111}\ \overline{148}\ \overline{62}\ \overline{37}\ \overline{122}$
$\overline{169}\ \overline{185}\ \overline{42}$

U Scarface actor. . . . .
$\overline{56}\ \overline{35}\ \overline{31}\ \overline{68}$

V Naval reply: 2 wds. . . . .
$\overline{89}\ \overline{152}\ \overline{80}\ \overline{127}\ \overline{172}\ \overline{117}$

W "Topsy-_____" . . . .
$\overline{70}\ \overline{49}\ \overline{158}\ \overline{19}\ \overline{182}$

X Author of The Fair Penitent and Jane Shore . . . . .
$\overline{167}\ \overline{5}\ \overline{108}\ \overline{93}$

Y "Get in _____"; repetitive routine: 2 wds. . . . . .
$\overline{188}\ \overline{197}\ \overline{91}\ \overline{83}$

1 M	2 Q	3 R	■	4 C	5 X	6 Q	7 L	■	8 D	9 A	10 O	11 B
12 B	13 S	■	14 L	15 R	16 T	■	17 A	18 G	19 W	20 J	21 H	■	22 E	23 B	24 I
■	25 F	26 I	27 O	28 E	■	29 S	30 G	■	31 U	32 A	■	33 O	34 Q	35 U	36 A
37 T	■	38 D	39 O	40 K	41 G	42 T	■	43 E	44 J	45 S	■	46 C	47 F	48 B	49 W
50 R	51 H	52 A	■	53 M	54 K	55 N	56 U	57 H	58 Q	59 B	■	60 N	61 P	62 T	63 I
64 D	■	65 F	66 P	67 R	68 U	69 K	■	70 W	71 I	72 A	■	73 A	74 H	75 O	76 S
77 D	78 L	79 I	80 V	■	81 D	82 O	■	83 Y	84 B	85 P	■	86 T	87 P	88 D	89 V
90 M	91 Y	92 P	93 X	94 H	■	95 G	96 C	97 L	■	98 S	99 A	100 E	■	101 I
102 S	103 R	104 H	105 J	106 G	107 Q	■	108 X	109 P	■	110 O	111 T	112 B	113 Q	■	114 A
115 J	116 G	117 V	■	118 R	119 C	120 H	■	121 J	122 T	123 C	124 L	■	125 M	126 L	127 V
128 E	129 F	■	130 P	131 T	132 B	■	133 M	134 L	135 B	136 I	137 R	■	138 C	139 P	140 G
141 Q	■	142 F	143 H	■	144 C	145 G	146 H	147 L	148 T	149 J	150 N	■	151 I	152 V
153 N	154 E	155 R	156 B	157 J	158 W	159 O	■	160 S	161 B	■	162 T	163 O	■	164 P	165 O
166 J	167 X	168 F	169 T	170 R	171 K	■	172 V	173 P	174 I	175 F	176 O	■	177 B	178 Q	179 F
180 K	181 M	182 W	■	183 E	184 O	185 T	■	186 I	187 J	188 Y	189 P	■	190 F	191 S
■	192 I	193 B	■	194 F	195 R	196 B	197 Y	■	198 A	199 L	200 E	201 H

The Disappearance of Lady Frances Carfax

135. For this Semi-Crostic, I've incorporated the clues into a short summary of our story.

The villain of the piece, the Rev. Dr. __ __ __ __ __ __ __ __ __ __ __

3 1 11 16 3 3 2 35 36 16 6

(944), known to his close friends and adversaries as __ __ __ __

1 37 11 22

__ __ __ __ __ __ (947), easily eludes the grip of the ardent romantic interest,

4 16 7 27 6 3

__ __ __ __ __ __ (946), then presents a legal death

4 26 8 20 18 15

__ __ __ __ __ __ __ __ __ __ (952) to Holmes, the "common

9 29 6 7 23 38 32 9 5 21 42

__ __ __ __ __ __ __" (951), but is nevertheless foiled in his distardly

28 10 6 30 33 12 6

attempts upon the lovely __ __ __ __ __ __ __ __ __ __ __ (943) by

39 19 47 44 38 6 46 41 17 49 14

our hero, who shall always remain __ __ __ __ __ __ __ __ __ __ __ (945).

34 43 45 10 24 25 13 48 40 31 50

Solution:

__ __ __ __ __ __ __ __ __ __ __ __ __

1 2 3 4 5 6 7 8 9 10 11 12 13

__ __ __ __ __ __ __ __ __ __ __ __ __ __

14 15 16 17 18 19 20 21 22 23 24 25 26 27

__ __ __ __ __ __ __ __ __ __ __ __ __ __ __ __ __

28 29 30 31 32 33 34 35 36 37 38 39 40 41 42 43 44

__ __ __ __ __ __. (947)

45 46 47 48 49 50

136. I just couldn't pare down this lovely sentiment, so here's a Super-Quotation.

H	E	C	C	C	A	A	I	D	A	E	A	C	D	A	F	E	E	A	L	D
H	I	N	E	L	C	I	N	E	M	H	A	N	L	A	M	E	E	A	N	T
L	O	T	E	R	I	M	S	E	S	L	N	R	T	U	M	H	E	G	S	T
S		O	T	L	U	T	I	T	Y	O	T			N	O	N	L			
Y			X	Y		W	N				U				S	S			S	

The Adventure of the Devil's Foot

137. Here's perhaps the most terrifying moment ever shared by our heroes, in a 34-word Hidden Phrase. (Additional hint: The first word begins with the 22nd letter of the alphabet.)

```
A  B  C  O  D  D  R  E  L  L  E  W  D  E  I
E  V  O  F  A  E  G  U  H  I  E  T  J  L  N
K  A  L  B  N  L  N  M  P  H  H  H  N  B  O
P  G  U  Q  D  R  T  H  R  O  T  R  V  A  S
T  U  V  W  S  I  Y  Z  H  A  N  E  E  K  G
A  E  B  H  C  W  M  S  Q  D  R  S  S  A  E
S  H  A  P  E  S  A  G  A  Y  S  H  O  E  F
H  I  J  D  H  K  A  M  G  L  H  O  P  F  F
O  C  A  N  T  H  I  E  Z  M  A  L  W  S  O
P  R  Q  N  D  D  C  N  R  P  D  D  S  N  T
K  C  L  O  U  D  B  A  N  K  O  W  T  U  I
U  V  E  P  W  Y  F  C  E  X  W  O  Y  O  E
E  C  L  B  E  A  L  E  A  N  D  U  D  Z  M
Z  D  B  E  X  C  F  Y  G  A  H  L  E  I  O
W  E  O  G  N  M  N  I  W  L  K  D  N  J  S
Q  P  T  N  T  Q  D  T  S  A  L  B  R  E  F
X  I  W  I  V  H  M  U  E  T  R  S  S  O  J
V  K  Y  M  Z  Y  E  A  D  V  E  N  T  A  B
R  C  U  O  D  S  O  U  L  E  L  F  I  G  M
P  J  N  C  M  V  L  K  K  R  J  E  I  N  H
V  X  O  G  N  I  H  T  E  M  O  S  F  O  G
```

5-6-7-3-4-4-3-4-9-4-1-6-3-1-7-2-9-6-3-6-2-4-11-7-4-3-9-5-4-6-5-5-2-4.

His Last Bow

138. Holmes's last case is, in many ways, the best of them all, despite the fact that Watson, owing to plot complications, had to write it in the third person. Here's a Word Detection for you with a short but so very fitting Mystery Quotation left over.

Air
Altamont
Asset

Baron Von Herling
Bell
Benz
Berlin
Blithe
Buffalo

Cable
Carlton Terrace
Claridge's Hotel

Dangling Prussian

Eagle

Finis
Foe

Gash
Goatee

Harwich
Hermit
His Last Bow
Hollis

Irish-American

Jack James
Junker

Kaiser
Key (3 times interlinked)

Lay
Low

Martha

Naval Signals

Open

Plans
Polo

Queen

Solent
Spy
Sussex Downs

Trap

Von Bork

Yacht

Zeppelin

```
B C C H I S L A S T B O W C W N
Y A O L A F F U B E L L A O A A
A B R G A I R L O B E R L I N V
C L O O N R I H O L L I S M N A
H E T I N T I P V T E S S A D L
T O S A H V E D O O U O C R R S
J Q H E M N O N G R N I F T E I
A U Y A K O T N P E R B Z H S G
C E N E R E N G H E S E O A I N
K E Y K R W N T M E P H L R A A
J N G R E I I A L P R O O G K L
A P A O L R H C E B S L L T A S
M C A G A S H L H D E N I O E E
E W N R I T I M R E H N A N A L
S A T R T N E L O S S O Z L G A
D N I S U S S E X D O W N S P Y
```

Mystery Quotation: __ __ __ __   __ __ __   __ __ __ __ __ __!

139. The Crossword grid here symbolizes the rays of the rising sun.
I imagine them warming the two elderly gentlemen as they have
their "last quiet talk" on the terrace. Some letters (sixteen in all)
are used only in one word rather than two in the puzzle. Upon
completion of the grid find these letters and scramble them
around to form the following phrase which explains why Holmes
could be diverted from his bees back to active service.

—— —— ——   —— ——   —— —— ——

—— —— —— —— —— —— ——

ACROSS

1 ". . . many of us may wither
  before its _____" (980)
6 "Same as I said in my _____"
  (975)
11 The month (970)
13 Von Bork never made it there
  (971)
14 General Bradley
15 Frilly
16 Author Lewis, "initially"
18 Lode load
19 _____ Kabibble
20 Hawaiian instrument
22 The chauffeur, familiarly
24 Continent: Abbr.
25 Adventurer Lawrence, "initially"
26 Foul, as Von Bork and Von Herling
27 _____ de cologne
29 Exclamation, cousin to tsk
30. ". . . he softly clapped his _____
  hands" (1973)
31 Author Munro, "initially"
33 Helen's adopted home
34 "There's an _____ wind coming, Watson" (980)
35 Egyptian sun-god
36 Become drowsy
37 Gender: Abbr.
38 Exist
39 Winnie was one
42 Mimicking bird
45 Accomplish
46 H's later years have been devoted
  to this charming insect (978)
47 Harem room
48 Mined find
50 Pencil necessity
52 Deciliter: Abbr.
53 Author Stevenson, "initially"
55 Known

57 "Now I _____ me down to
  sleep"
58 Pronoun
59 Track advice
61 Pronoun, familiarly French
62 "England may leave France to
  her _____" (972)
63 41 Down, for sure
65 "So far as I can judge the trend
  of _____" (971)
67 ". . . all the devoted _____ of
  the Kaiser" (971)
69 Singer Newman
70 Wreck; waif: Fr.

DOWN

1 Boat, ship: Span.
2 Lutetium, in chemistry
3 Past
4 Japanese wrestler
5 Nicholas and Alexander
6 Stop
7 Fallen or Triumphal
8 Adverbial suffix
9 Chinese measure
10 Boredom
12 ". . . there is no binding _____
  between them" (972)
13 "You look the same _____ boy
  as ever" (978)
17 H. Rider Haggard work
20 Army rank: Abbr.
21 Lotta man! (anagramatically)
22 England, to the krauts: 2 wds.
23 The Confessions of _____
  Turner: Styron
26 Consume
28 Abraham's birthplace
30 Fleet surgeon: Abbr.
32 Garden tool

35 "... one blood-_____ gash like
an open wound" (970)
39 Foot: prefix or suffix
40 Old English: Abbr.
41 21 Down, minus the disguise
42 "She might almost personify
Britannia" (974)
43 Negative
44 Sandy's sound
46 "... the lights of the shipping
glimmered in the _____" (971)
49 "It h'ain't the _____, h'it's the
'umidity."

51 Anxious; impatient
52 "It was the favourite _____ of
the lamented" (979)
54 Feudally, 22 Down to 41 Down
56 "... God's _____ hung heavy
over a degenerate world" (970)
58 Out or over or down or in or on
60 College training, for short
62 Swamp; bog
64 "Three _____ match": 2 wds.
66 Servicemen's hospital: Abbr.
68 The vast wasteland: Abbr.

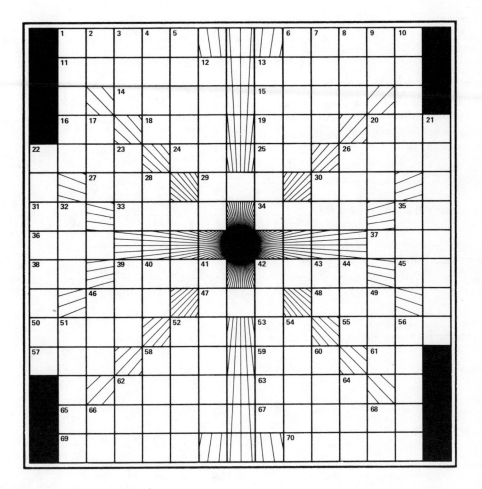

The Adventure of the Illustrious Client

140. Our tale spans a wider social range than any other in the Canon, from Letter V to the very peak of British royalty. It's also one of the grimmest tales, as I hope my Clue Line and Quotation will show.

Clues

A The subject of our quotation: Full name . . . .
94 117 135 167 173 207 15 21 26
184 200 38 62 131 145 90 104
110 211

B Bones or days of summer . . . .
11 22 28 179

C Our subject's looks were almost this (996) . . . . . .
1 12 19 33 46 56 74 107

D Pod vegetable . . . .
112 109 182 8

E Actor Howard _____ . . . .
30 63 84 96

F Where Violet met Mr. Wrong (986) . . . .
5 10 70 137 149 192 203 174

G Sir James was this sort of word to W (984) . . . . . .
18 34 122 148 157 177 195 215 191

H "Excuse my _____, Mr. Holmes," sneered the Austrian murderer (988) . . . .
40 53 168 193 210 78 92 127 141

I It was ripped off a one-legged vendor at Charing Cross: Comp. (933) . . . .
164 181 7 66 93 140 143 189 31

J Argument . . . .
44 101 115 125 209 6

K The 1902 date our story opens: 2 wds. . . . .
41 3 171 128 134 206 214 37 42
91 142 202 64 77

L ". . . I'll go _____ off him": W's offer to H, 4 wds. (994) . . . .
27 49 75 119 150 187 14 111 204
20 32 58 68 72 82 85

M Another name for the vendor in Letter I . . . .
89 99 100 155 213 54

N Duchamp's school . . . .
55 61 158 163

O Roy Bean, the _____ the Pecos: 3 wds. . . . .
185 45 67 136 175 156 162 197 50

P Worn out . . . .
60 121 166 178 35 81

Q Face part . . . .
139 71 79 23

R Hernando's for one . . . .
36 48 201 216 76 180 144 16

S Ireland . . . .
13 147 102 161

T Apply the cloth again . . . .
188 95 160 108 124 116

U Trisectional plot of grass. . . . .
$\overline{97}$ $\overline{205}$ $\overline{176}$ $\overline{59}$ $\overline{126}$ $\overline{183}$ $\overline{169}$ $\overline{24}$

V Where Shinwell dived in search of "garbage in the darker recesses" (988) . . . .
$\overline{118}$ $\overline{130}$ $\overline{47}$ $\overline{65}$ $\overline{98}$ $\overline{86}$ $\overline{132}$ $\overline{212}$ $\overline{196}$

$\overline{190}$

W Hawk's swoop to prey, or a drunk . . . .
$\overline{9}$ $\overline{105}$ $\overline{198}$ $\overline{170}$ $\overline{29}$

X Cowboy Lash _____ . . . .
$\overline{123}$ $\overline{52}$ $\overline{199}$ $\overline{186}$ $\overline{114}$

Y All H's "hot words" could not stand up to these: 3 wds. . . . .
$\overline{120}$ $\overline{51}$ $\overline{172}$ $\overline{133}$ $\overline{103}$ $\overline{73}$ $\overline{129}$ $\overline{87}$

Z Two criminal artists or artistic criminals: 3 wds. .
$\overline{153}$ $\overline{4}$ $\overline{83}$ $\overline{194}$ $\overline{43}$ $\overline{159}$ $\overline{2}$ $\overline{165}$ $\overline{17}$

$\overline{151}$ $\overline{69}$ $\overline{208}$ $\overline{39}$ $\overline{80}$ $\overline{138}$ $\overline{25}$ $\overline{57}$

$\overline{146}$

Z_1 Lord: master . . . .
$\overline{152}$ $\overline{106}$ $\overline{154}$ $\overline{113}$ $\overline{88}$

	1 C	2 Z	3 K		4 Z	5 F	6 J			7 I	8 D	9 W							
	10 F	11 B	12 C	13 S	14 L	15 A	16 R		17 Z	18 G	19 C	20 L	21 A						
	22 B	23 Q	24 U		25 Z	26 A	27 L	28 B	29 W	30 E			31 I	32 L					
33 C		34 G	35 P	36 R	37 K	38 A		39 Z	40 H	41 K			42 K	43 Z					
44 J		45 O	46 C	47 V		48 R	49 L	50 O	51 Y	52 X	53 H	54 M	55 N		56 C				
57 Z	58 L		59 U	60 P	61 N	62 A	63 E	64 K	65 V	66 I		67 O	68 L	69 Z	70 F				
71 Q		72 L		73 Y	74 C	75 L		76 R	77 K	78 H	79 Q	80 Z	81 P	82 L					
83 Z		84 E	85 L	86 V		87 Y	88 Z_1	89 M	90 A	91 K	92 H	93 I		94 A	95 T				
96 E	97 U	98 V	99 M		100 M	101 J	102 S	103 Y		104 A	105 W	106 Z_1		107 C	108 T				
109 D	110 A		111 L	112 D	113 Z_1	114 X		115 J	116 T	117 A	118 V	119 L	120 Y	121 P	122 G				
123 X		124 T	125 J	126 U	127 H	128 K	129 Y	130 V	131 A		132 V	133 Y	134 K	135 A					
136 O	137 F	138 Z	139 Q	140 I		141 H	142 K	143 I		144 R	145 A	146 Z	147 S	148 G	149 F				
	150 L	151 Z	152 Z_1		153 Z	154 Z_1	155 M	156 O	157 G	158 N		159 Z		160 T	161 S				
162 O		163 N	164 I	165 Z		166 P	167 A	168 H	169 U		170 W	171 K	172 Y	173 A	174 F				
175 O		176 U	177 G	178 P	179 B		180 R	181 I	182 D	183 U		184 A	185 O	186 X	187 L				
188 T	189 I	190 V		191 G	192 F	193 H	194 Z	195 G	196 V	197 O	198 W	199 X	200 A	201 R					
202 K	203 F	204 L	205 U	206 K	207 A	208 Z		209 J	210 H	211 A	212 V	213 M	214 K	215 G	216 R				

The Adventure of the Blanched Soldier

141. Here are three cryptic lists from our tale, with different codes for each.

People	Places	Things (Hint: You'll find at least one "E" in each entry.)
LCODU FNFF	CNSSBTITW	ANDQ VEQ
BNKNMDK	JMHELCEHJED	DKDTGEMS FZM
DOUVNQSG	IJHTTJ	SETDRSQX
NKF QCKRG	JZWQZHV EBS	UNXEFD
OQ. JDMS	FPHA	BGDDRD
ACKFZ UHORUNM	IEZJM PKHNRP	VDDOKHDR
CMFDQUNM	FHTJEHNP	KDTDQ
UHQ LCODU	QTSKEHSIMNHT	
UCTMFDQU	QZKKTBIIFHZNJ	

142. Here's a variation on a Scramblegram. Both 16-word sentences hiding below are in their proper order. All punctuation is correct. It's just that I've written a word or two (or more) of one sentence, then some of the other, then back to the first, etc. You merely have to slip them apart.

Alas, I see that I should have no more to show than you, but I have trained my hand so when I tell myself to notice what my own story! I see.

143. Holmesian modesty.

I	E	I	I	G	S	M	A	D	A	O	S	I
N	H	M	N	S	T	O	T	H	B	T	W	I
S	T	S	S		T	R	Y	K	E	U		
T			Y						N			

The Adventure of the Mazarin Stone

144. A couple of fine Holmesian put-downs from an otherwise sadly negligible tale.

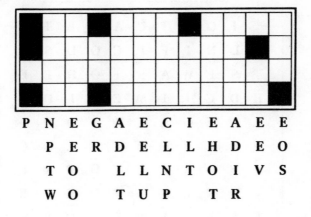

```
P  N  E  G  A  E  C  I  E  A  E  E
   P  E  R  D  E  L  L  H  D  E  O
   T  O     L  L  N  T  O  I  V  S
   W  O     T  U  P     T  R
```

145.

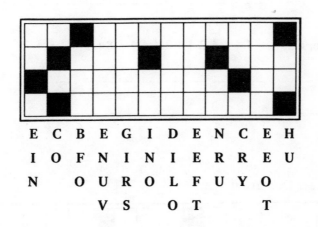

```
E  C  B  E  G  I  D  E  N  C  E  H
I  O  F  N  I  N  I  E  R  R  E  U
N     O  U  R  O  L  F  U  Y  O
      V  S     O  T        T
```

146. Look for the internal clues in these anagrammatic renderings of several people and one thing from our story.

1. Gun nott toy. Vile curses. (5, 8, 7)
2. As iz—ornament. (7, 5)
3. Mean sort, M? (3, 6)
4. T: "Con D Earl, Merle." (4, 10)
5. Ba! Rue ze Sten! (11)
6. Seen risk day. (4, 7)
7. I'm risen, I'm pert. (5, 8)
8. Ar! Me they score. (4, 9)
9. Molls shock here. (8, 6)

The Adventure of the Three Gables

147. A variation on the old Hidden Phrase. The leftover grid letters, transcribed from left to right, top to bottom into the spaces below, will spell out another quotation from our story. Be careful! Some words you can read right off the grid may be a part of this second quotation.

```
      I  O  Y  T  U  A  E  B  T
   S  D  N  I  F  F  C  O  U  S  R
   T  S  E  W  A  S  T  O  H  E  E
   H  D  C  T  I  M  E  F  L  D  M
   E  A  E  O  A  T  W  I  O  U  O
   H  H  L  F  M  H  F  H  E  O  C
   A  Y  D  A  L  E  T  O  R  L
   L  H  N  E  H  W  T  H  E  P  E
   F  E  E  V  E  N  L  A  M  B  W
      L  I  G  H  T  M  O  R  E
```

Letter Count: 3-4-3-4-2-4-4-2-4-4-4-3-8-6-5-3-4-5-4-7.

—, —— ————, ——— ——

————; —— ——— ———.

148. A Super-Quotation.

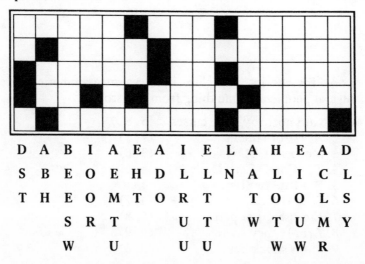

```
D  A  B  I  A  E  A  I  E  L  A  H  E  A  D
S  B  E  O  E  H  D  L  L  N  A  L  I  C  L
T  H  E  O  M  T  O  R  T     T  O  O  L  S
   S  R  T        U  T     W  T  U  M  Y
   W     U        U  U        W  W  R
```

The Adventure of the Sussex Vampire

149. A father's cry.

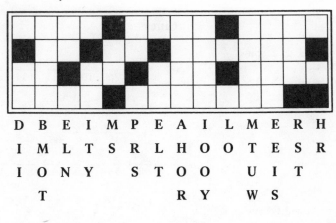

```
D B E I M P E A I L M E R H
I M L T S R L H O O T E S R
I O N Y   S T O O   U I T
T         R Y   W S
```

150. Cold comfort.

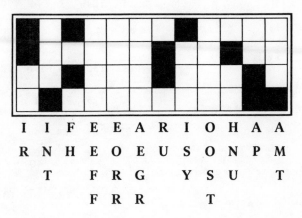

```
I I F E E A R I O H A A
R N H E O E U S O N P M
  T   F R G   Y S U   T
      F R R     T
```

151. And the nastiest little varmint since Tonga.

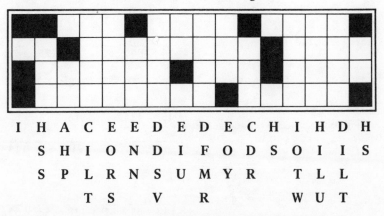

```
I H A C E E D E D E C H I H D H
S H I O N D I F O D S O I I S
S P L R N S U M Y R   T L L
  T S   V   R     W U T
```

152. Domestic bliss restored, and Holmes comments on the supernatural.

Clues

A "A fall in childhood and a _____ spine,
Mr. Holmes" (1037). . . . .

<u>13</u> <u>96</u> <u>104</u> <u>111</u> <u>134</u> <u>141</u> <u>162</u>

B "I want my child. I _____ my child": 4 wds.
(1041). . . . .

<u>183</u> <u>10</u> <u>61</u> <u>81</u> <u>97</u> <u>121</u> <u>122</u> <u>4</u> <u>23</u>

<u>45</u> <u>67</u> <u>87</u>

C Horse . . . .

<u>92</u> <u>58</u> <u>129</u> <u>131</u> <u>139</u> <u>150</u>

D Quick sniff. . . . .

<u>170</u> <u>179</u> <u>17</u> <u>72</u> <u>154</u>

E " 'She will not see me,' cried Ferguson. '_____,'
said Holmes": 4 wds. (1042) . . . .

<u>165</u> <u>29</u> <u>76</u> <u>85</u> <u>102</u> <u>118</u> <u>149</u> <u>177</u> <u>9</u>

<u>36</u> <u>108</u> <u>132</u>

F ". . . the ancient tiles . . . were marked with the
_____": 4 wds. (1039). . . . .

<u>166</u> <u>184</u> <u>25</u> <u>44</u> <u>70</u> <u>89</u> <u>147</u> <u>155</u> <u>28</u>

<u>38</u> <u>62</u> <u>110</u> <u>6</u> <u>26</u>

G ". . . but not as your daughter may conceive:
friend, _____": Hamlet, 2½ wds. . . . .

<u>142</u> <u>152</u> <u>181</u> <u>176</u> <u>22</u> <u>30</u> <u>50</u>

H Hussy; wench . . . .

<u>57</u> <u>125</u> <u>93</u> <u>21</u>

I ". . . a very good, a very loving and a very _____":
3 wds. (1043). . . . .

<u>32</u> <u>161</u> <u>164</u> <u>5</u> <u>37</u> <u>49</u> <u>16</u> <u>115</u> <u>128</u>

<u>84</u> <u>135</u> <u>40</u>

J ". . . this note is merely to give you a general idea
of the _____" (1035) . . . .

<u>12</u> <u>60</u> <u>79</u> <u>90</u> <u>103</u> <u>151</u> <u>156</u> <u>163</u> <u>8</u>

K ". . . leaning over the baby and apparently _____.":
3 wds. (1035). . . . .

<u>143</u> <u>171</u> <u>174</u> <u>64</u> <u>74</u> <u>19</u> <u>158</u> <u>69</u> <u>78</u>

<u>101</u> <u>120</u> <u>51</u> <u>136</u>

L ". . . when I threw you over the ropes _____":
3 wds. (1037). . . . .

<u>83</u> <u>113</u> <u>157</u> <u>7</u> <u>47</u> <u>106</u> <u>167</u> <u>75</u> <u>63</u>

<u>100</u> <u>130</u> <u>41</u>

M Sumatra inhabitant: 2 wds. (1034) . . . .

<u>34</u> <u>94</u> <u>55</u> <u>124</u> <u>178</u> <u>185</u> <u>14</u> <u>98</u>

N Parisian architect. . . . .

<u>2</u> <u>117</u> <u>86</u> <u>159</u> <u>53</u> <u>172</u>

O The Bagel _____: New York restaurant chain . . . .

<u>15</u> <u>43</u> <u>42</u> <u>116</u>

P ". . . traits quite alien to her _____ sweet and gentle
disposition" (1035) . . . .

<u>107</u> <u>3</u> <u>27</u> <u>71</u> <u>33</u> <u>114</u> <u>48</u> <u>77</u> <u>173</u>

<u>127</u>

Q Develop, as action . . . .

<u>160</u> <u>65</u> <u>1</u> <u>138</u> <u>133</u> <u>105</u>

R Family member: Sl. . . . .
$\overline{66}$ $\overline{88}$ $\overline{175}$ $\overline{109}$ $\overline{119}$ $\overline{11}$

S "La belle Dame sans Merci _____ in thrall": Keats, 2 wds. . . . .
$\overline{52}$ $\overline{73}$ $\overline{82}$ $\overline{35}$ $\overline{95}$ $\overline{80}$ $\overline{137}$ $\overline{180}$

T Pocket watch accessories. . . . .
$\overline{123}$ $\overline{144}$ $\overline{20}$ $\overline{46}$

U Oberlin College state . . . .
$\overline{146}$ $\overline{68}$ $\overline{112}$ $\overline{153}$

V Most new; most rare. . . . .
$\overline{91}$ $\overline{39}$ $\overline{126}$ $\overline{140}$ $\overline{168}$ $\overline{182}$

W "Rich gifts wax poor when givers prove _____": Ophelia. . . . .
$\overline{59}$ $\overline{56}$ $\overline{31}$ $\overline{169}$ $\overline{18}$ $\overline{54}$

X Mulligan, for one. . . . .
$\overline{99}$ $\overline{148}$ $\overline{24}$ $\overline{145}$

1 Q	2 N	3 P	4 B	5 I	6 F	7 L	8 J		9 E	10 B	11 R
	12 J	13 A	14 M	15 O	16 I	17 D	18 W	19 K	20 T	21 H	
22 G	23 B	24 X		25 F	26 F	27 P		28 F	29 E	30 G	31 W	32 I	33 P	34 M
35 S	36 E	37 I		38 F	39 V	40 I	41 L	42 O		43 O	44 F	45 B	46 T	47 L
48 P	49 I	50 G	51 K	52 S	53 N	54 W		55 M	56 W	57 H		58 C	59 W	60 J	61 B
62 F	63 L	64 K	65 Q	66 R		67 B	68 U	69 K	70 F		71 P		72 D	73 S	74 K
75 L	76 E		77 P	78 K		79 J	80 S	81 B		82 S	83 L	84 I	85 E		86 N
87 B	88 R		89 F	90 J	91 V		92 C	93 H	94 M	95 S		96 A	97 B	98 M	99 X
100 L	101 K		102 E	103 J	104 A	105 Q		106 L	107 P	108 E	109 R	110 F	111 A		112 U
113 L		114 P		115 I	116 O	117 N	118 E	119 R	120 K	121 B		122 B	123 T		124 M
125 H	126 V		127 P	128 I	129 C		130 L	131 C	132 E	133 Q		134 A	135 I	136 K	137 S
	138 Q	139 C	140		141 A	142 G	143 K	144 T	145 X		146 U	147 F		148 X	149 E
150 C		151 J	152 G	153 U		154 D	155 F	156 J	157 L	158 K	159 N	160 Q	161 I		162 A
163 J	164 I	165 E	166 F	167 L	168 V		169 W		170 D	171 K	172 N	173 P		174 K	175 R
176 G	177 E		178 M	179 D	180 S		181 G	182 V	183 B	184 F	185 M			

The Adventure of the Three Garridebs

153. A super-semi-crostic. Try to do this one in order. It gives a nice pattern to the development of the solution.

Definitions

A Alexander _____ Garrideb . . .

B . . . made some of his money in the _____ of Chicago: 2 wds.

C The town John G. claimed as home

D Its "mayor" in 1890 . . .

E . . . who "is still _____."

F John G's "profession"

G W remarked upon these in Little Ryder Street

H Where Nathan occasionally went

I This, found in a newspaper . . .

J . . . apparently written by _____ Garrideb . . .

K . . . had this misspelled . . .

L . . . sending Nathan on this "wild-goose."

M _____ and Steele, house-agents . . .

N . . . confirmed the name of this previous tenant . . .

O . . . whom H knew to be this . . .

P . . . and led to this fellow's capture . . .

Q By our hero, _____

Words

$\overline{10}\ \overline{4}\ \overline{27}\ \overline{1}\ \overline{53}\ \overline{9}\ \overline{7}\ \overline{15}$

$\overline{3}\ \overline{26}\ \overline{45}\ \overline{4}\ \overline{2}\ \overline{48}\ \overline{1}\ \overline{18}$

$\overline{25}\ \overline{7}\ \overline{48}\ \overline{45}\ \overline{39}\ \overline{4}$

$\overline{53}\ \overline{30}\ \overline{5}\ \overline{4}\ \overline{15}\ \overline{16}\ \overline{45}\ \overline{8}\ \overline{5}\ \overline{37}\ \overline{11}\ \overline{8}\ \overline{8}$

$\overline{44}\ \overline{7}\ \overline{15}\ \overline{7}\ \overline{14}\ \overline{8}\ \overline{45}\ \overline{35}$

$\overline{53}\ \overline{20}\ \overline{6}\ \overline{74}\ \overline{45}\ \overline{8}$

$\overline{53}\ \overline{13}\ \overline{12}\ \overline{19}\ \overline{1}\ \overline{29}\ \overline{46}\ \overline{23}\ \overline{22}\ \overline{5}$

$\overline{5}\ \overline{32}\ \overline{43}\ \overline{50}\ \overline{45}\ \overline{75}\ \overline{59}\ \overline{5}$

$\overline{28}\ \overline{80}\ \overline{65}\ \overline{45}\ \overline{8}\ \overline{49}\ \overline{17}\ \overline{5}\ \overline{45}\ \overline{89}\ \overline{45}\ \overline{34}\ \overline{58}$

$\overline{68}\ \overline{38}\ \overline{42}\ \overline{56}\ \overline{8}\ \overline{62}$

$\overline{48}\ \overline{53}\ \overline{41}\ \overline{42}\ \overline{21}$

$\overline{70}\ \overline{71}\ \overline{60}\ \overline{36}\ \overline{45}$

$\overline{77}\ \overline{51}\ \overline{53}\ \overline{57}\ \overline{54}\ \overline{67}\ \overline{73}\ \overline{55}$

$\overline{31}\ \overline{83}\ \overline{63}\ \overline{88}\ \overline{8}\ \overline{64}\ \overline{40}$

$\overline{85}\ \overline{86}\ \overline{33}\ \overline{61}\ \overline{81}\ \overline{45}\ \overline{8}\ \overline{52}\ \overline{45}\ \overline{69}\ \overline{84}\ \overline{47}\ \overline{8}$

$\overline{92}\ \overline{78}\ \overline{72}\ \overline{87}\ \overline{66}\ \overline{24}\ \overline{76}\ \overline{65}\ \overline{90}\ \overline{79}\ \overline{91}$

$\overline{82}$

Solution:

$\overline{1}\ \overline{2}\ \overline{3}\ \overline{4}\ \overline{5}\ \overline{6}\ \overline{7}\ \overline{8}\ \overline{9}\ \overline{10}\ \overline{11}\ \overline{12}\ \overline{13}\ \overline{14}\ \overline{15}\ \overline{16}\ \overline{17}\ \overline{18}\ \overline{19}\ \overline{20}\ \overline{21}\ \overline{22}\ \overline{23}\ \overline{24}\ \overline{25}\ \overline{26}$

$\overline{27}\ \overline{28}\ \overline{29}\ \overline{30}\ \overline{31}\ \overline{32}\ \overline{33}\ \overline{34}\ \overline{35}\ \overline{36}\ \overline{37}\ \overline{38}\ \overline{39}\ \overline{40}\ \overline{41}\ \overline{42}\ \overline{43}\ \overline{44}\ \overline{45}\ \overline{46}\ \overline{47}\ \overline{48}\ \overline{49}\ \overline{50}\ \overline{51}\ \overline{52}$

$\overline{53}\ \overline{54}\ \overline{55}\ \overline{56}\ \overline{57}\ \overline{58}\ \overline{59}\ \overline{60}\ \overline{61}\ \overline{62}\ \overline{63}\ \overline{64}\ \overline{65}\ \overline{66}\ \overline{67}\ \overline{68}\ \overline{69}\ \overline{70}\ \overline{71}\ \overline{72}\ \overline{73}\ \overline{74}$

$\overline{75}\ \overline{76}\ \overline{77}\ \overline{78}\ \overline{79}\ \overline{80}\ \overline{81}\ \overline{82}\ \overline{83}\ \overline{84}\ \overline{85}\ \overline{86}\ \overline{87}\ \overline{88}\ \overline{89}\ \overline{90}\ \overline{91}\ \overline{92}$

154. A bit of a farce, too.

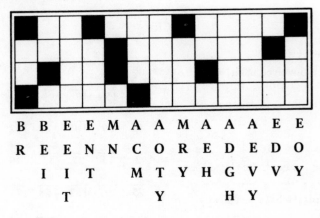

```
B  B  E  E  M  A  A  M  A  A  A  E  E
R  E  E  N  N  C  O  R  E  D  E  D  O
   I  I  T     M  T  Y  H  G  V  V  Y
      T        Y        H  Y
```

155. Holmes: noble in defeat and sarcastic in victory.

```
D  A  A  E  E  P  E  E  E  A  F  T  E
W  H  A  T  J  T  R  T  S  E  N  T  R
W  S  S  T     U  S  S  W  L  N  U
      W        W           Y  O
```

156. Best turn of phrase since the "Chin·China coaster."

```
E  B  I  E  E  E  A  A  B  A  G  B  H
O  H  Q  O  F  C  R  I  N  H  M  E  H
T  N  T  S  R     R     T  U     T  O
U        U     W        Z  Y
```

The Problem of Thor Bridge

157.   This one raises an old problem I'll be dealing with later.

Clues

A She was lost in the mist (1054) . . . .

<u> </u> <u> </u> <u> </u> <u> </u> <u> </u> <u> </u>
1   50   64   112   117   138

B "I am getting into your involved habit, Watson, of telling a story ____" (1056) . . . .

151   159   176   93   104   8   13   34

C "No, no, Watson, I will not ____ it is possible": 2 wds. (1065). . . . .

42   69   101   127   162   173   130   96   77

D "I fear it is a ____ business" (1056) . . . .

2   15   27   53   149   63   72   83   89

E "____ is innocent and . . . has to be cleared": 2 wds. (1058). . . . .

95   107   131   158   171   20   109   147   43

F Immediately afterward: Arch. (a *very* handy acrostic word). . . . .

47   84   123   32   29   155   136

G Ancient Germanic alphabet character . . . .

5   59   87   141

H "A man may fish with the worm that hath ____": Hamlet, 4 wds. . . . .

145   33   66   80   119   143   168   177   19

100

I Thanks: Ger. . . . .

70   91   99   52   153

J What the bridge spanned: 2 wds. (1057) . . . .

14   26   35   40   157   181   60   165

K "And women lead an ____ and may do things beyond the judgment of a man": 2 wds. (1061) . .

4   56   129   150   97   142   51   75   125

178

L "Monads have ____," according to Leibniz: 2 wds. . . . .

61   85   11   23   122   103   115   154   175

M Sleepy, for one . . . .

161   48   62   148   18

N "It's the damned ____ of it all that makes me crazy" (1056). . . . .

31   167   57   71   9   111   139   132   39

O Belle's ploy, in a pinch . . . .

76   55   121   135   169

P He went back for his umbrella (1054) . . . .

38   3   98   73   152   105   128   170   36

22

Q ". . . I shall have shaken off his ____ slavery" (1057). . . . .

67   134   180   86   92   41   10   6

R Second part of a countdown: 4 wds. . . . .

137   81   12   30   17   120   21   46   49

24   133   54   78

S Tots or earls' equals. . . . .

7   124   166   140   25   94

T How Gibson often treated the Mrs. . . . .

79   37   144   65   113   74   16

1 A		2 D	3 P	4 K	5 G	6 Q		7 S	8 B	9 N	10 Q		11 L	12 R	13 B
14 J	15 D	16 T		17 R	18 M		19 H	20 E	21 R	22 P		23 L	24 R		25 S
26 J	27 D	28 U		29 F	30 R		31 N	32 F	33 H	34 B	35 J	36 P	37 T		38 P
39 N	40 J	41 Q	42 C	43 E	44 W		45 V	46 R	47 F		48 M	49 R	50 A	51 K	
52 I	53 D	54 R	55 O	56 K		57 N	58 V	59 G	60 J	61 L	62 M	63 D	64 A	65 T	66 H
	67 Q	68 U	69 C		70 I	71 N	72 D	73 P	74 T	75 K	76 O	77 C		78 R	79 T
80 H		81 R	82 U	83 D		84 F	85 L	86 Q	87 G	88 U		89 D	90 W	91 I	92 Q
93 B		94 S	95 E	96 C	97 K	98 P	99 I	100 H		101 C	102 U	103 L		104 B	105 P
106 V	107 E		108 U		109 E	110 W	111 N	112 A	113 T		114 U	115 L	116 W		117 A
118 U		119 H	120 R	121 O	122 L	123 F		124 S	125 K		126 W	127 C	128 P		129 K
130 C	131 E	132 N	133 R		134 Q	135 O	136 F	137 R	138 A	139 N	140 S	141 G	142 K		143 H
	144 T	145 H	146 U	147 E	148 M	149 D	150 K	151 B	152 P	153 I		154 L	155 F	156 U	157 J
	158 E	159 B	160 U	161 M		162 C	163 V		164 U	165 J		166 S	167 N	168 H	169 O
170 P	171 E	172 U		173 C	174 U		175 L	176 B	177 H	178 K	179 W	180 Q	181 J		

The Adventure of the Creeping Man

158. Part of a most interesting self-study.

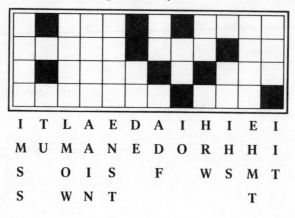

```
I  T  L  A  E  D  A  I  H  I  E  I
M  U  M  A  N  E  D  O  R  H  H  I
S     O  I  S     F     W  S  M  T
S     W  N  T              T
```

159. A Holmesian *reductio ad absurdum*.

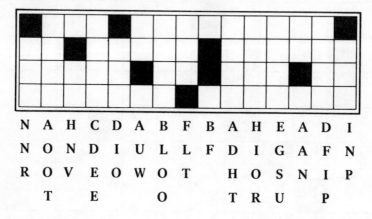

```
N  A  H  C  D  A  B  F  B  A  H  E  A  D  I
N  O  N  D  I  U  L  L  F  D  I  G  A  F  N
R  O  V  E  O  W  O  T     H  O  S  N  I  P
   T     E     O           T  R  U     P
```

160. "It would be the survival of the least fit."

```
C  E  A  L  D  O  B  E  C  M  A  E
N  H  R  S  O  S  O  L  P  O  M  F
W  O  S  T  P  U  O  R  T  O  O  R
W  O  T        R           O  Y
```

The Adventure of the Lion's Mane

161. As before, our Hidden Phrase, once found, will reveal another quotation from our tale.

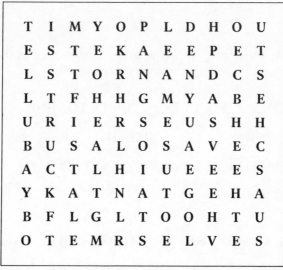

T	I	M	Y	O	P	L	D	H	O	U
E	S	T	E	K	A	E	E	P	E	T
L	S	T	O	R	N	A	N	D	C	S
L	T	F	H	H	G	M	Y	A	B	E
U	R	I	E	R	S	E	U	S	H	H
B	U	S	A	L	O	S	A	V	E	C
A	C	T	L	H	I	U	E	E	E	S
Y	K	A	T	N	A	T	G	E	H	A
B	F	L	G	L	T	O	O	H	T	U
O	T	E	M	R	S	E	L	V	E	S

Letter Count: 5-4-7-3-5-7-2-2-4-2-2-6-2-1-6.

—, — — — — — — — — — — — — — — — —, — — — — —

— — — — — — — — — — — — — — — — — — —

— — — — — — — — —.

162. I have a friend just like him — drives me crazy.

E G E E A B E F A C E D H
I G H O N E N M R D M R O R
L H I   S I O T S O U T   S
  I V   S   S   T

163. A real challenge for you, as it was for Holmes.

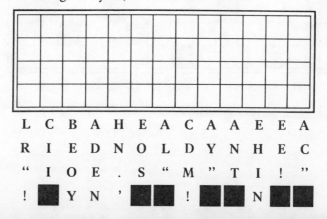

L C B A H E A C A A E A
R I E D N O L D Y N H E C
" I O E . S " M " T I ! "
! ▣ Y N ' ▣ ▣ ! ▣ ▣ N ▣

The Adventure of the Veiled Lodger

164. One of the most contemplative and pitiful stories in the Canon, as our Cryptograms and Quotations illustrate.

QEH VDZR MG GDQH DSH LOAHHA EDSA QM

XOAHSRQDOA. LG QEHSH LR OMQ RMPH

BMPNHORDQLMO EHSHDGQHS, QEHO QEH VMSIA LR

D BSXHI KHRQ.

165. RFG GVCOMJG NH MCRKGPR ZWHHGTKPE KZ KP

KRZGJH RFG ONZR MTGAKNWZ NH CJJ JGZZNPZ

RN CP KOMCRKGPR UNTJB.

166.

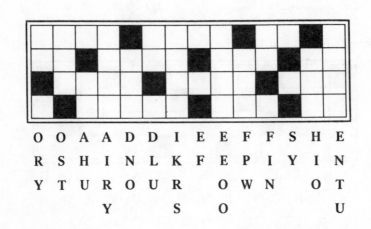

```
O  O  A  A  D  D  I  E  E  F  F  S  H  E
R  S  H  I  N  L  K  F  E  P  I  Y  I  N
Y  T  U  R  O  U  R     O  W  N     O  T
      Y        S        O           U
```

167.

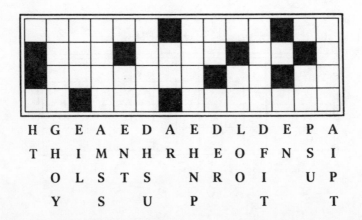

```
H  G  E  A  E  D  A  E  D  L  D  E  P  A
T  H  I  M  N  H  R  H  E  O  F  N  S  I
   O  L  S  T  S     N  R  O  I     U  P
   Y     S     U     P        T     T
```

The Adventure of Shoscombe Old Place

168. Again, hidden clues in the anagrammed names of people, one place and a couple of things should help you on to your solutions.

1. My Mum?	(5)
2. Warm Beers	(3,6)
3. Man no josh!	(4,5)
4. No hags mourn	(6,5)
5. Ssh! Joe in a bar.	(6,6)
6. Trail Ann and *go*!	(5,8)
7. Comb. hopes risen, C?	(9,6)
8. Locals' home: Ope'd B.C.'s	(9,3,5)
9. Torn Bob/Risen terror	(3,6,9)
10. Cry! It a far dead belle!	(4,8,6)

169. The unflappable Mason!

The Adventure of the Retired Colourman

170. Holmes twits his Boswell.

Definitions	Words
Where Amberley lived	$\overline{49}\ \overline{11}\ \overline{15}\ \overline{1}\ \overline{25}\ \overline{32}\ \overline{3}\ \overline{86}$
His chess mate (and cuckolder)	$\overline{67}\ \overline{3}\ \overline{12}\ \overline{11}\ \overline{67}\ \overline{47}\ \overline{11}\ \overline{25}\ \overline{55}$
"Our client has a few outward graces, whatever his _____ may be" 2 wds.	$\overline{1}\ \overline{101}\ \overline{47}\ \overline{11}\ \overline{67}\ \overline{76}\ \overline{1}\ \overline{67}\ \overline{55}\ \overline{14}$ $\overline{11}\ \overline{25}$
"What will you do?—if you will be good enough to _____ me"	$\overline{14}\ \overline{91}\ \overline{70}\ \overline{11}\ \overline{67}\ \overline{25}\ \overline{55}\ \overline{60}\ \overline{70}\ \overline{52}$
"I am preoccupied with this case of the two _____": 2 wds.	$\overline{7}\ \overline{13}\ \overline{19}\ \overline{55}\ \overline{1}\ \overline{73}\ \overline{19}\ \overline{3}\ \overline{55}\ \overline{67}$ $\overline{33}\ \overline{3}\ \overline{67}\ \overline{98}\ \overline{40}\ \overline{25}$
A great pot of this at The Haven: 2 wds.	$\overline{48}\ \overline{67}\ \overline{11}\ \overline{11}\ \overline{78}\ \overline{5}\ \overline{62}\ \overline{22}\ \overline{29}\ \overline{55}$
Amberley's excuse for the above: 2 wds.	$\overline{3}\ \overline{64}\ \overline{42}\ \overline{90}\ \overline{69}\ \overline{24}\ \overline{16}\ \overline{20}\ \overline{53}\ \overline{82}$ $\overline{55}$
The death-trap	$\overline{25}\ \overline{55}\ \overline{71}\ \overline{13}\ \overline{4}\ \overline{102}\ \overline{10}\ \overline{13}\ \overline{85}\ \overline{86}$
"Only this: what did you do _____?": 3 wds.	$\overline{37}\ \overline{75}\ \overline{88}\ \overline{65}\ \overline{28}\ \overline{80}\ \overline{43}\ \overline{58}\ \overline{30}\ \overline{70}$ $\overline{94}\ \overline{96}\ \overline{93}$
"He clapped his hands to his lips as if to _____": 3 wds.	$\overline{84}\ \overline{8}\ \overline{17}\ \overline{27}\ \overline{59}\ \overline{72}\ \overline{50}\ \overline{2}\ \overline{66}\ \overline{46}$ $\overline{35}\ \overline{99}$
". . . he suspected an _____"	$\overline{6}\ \overline{34}\ \overline{39}\ \overline{21}\ \overline{38}\ \overline{92}\ \overline{9}\ \overline{74}$
"And what is left in our _____?": 4 wds.	$\overline{56}\ \overline{100}\ \overline{23}\ \overline{51}\ \overline{36}\ \overline{81}\ \overline{41}\ \overline{54}\ \overline{89}\ \overline{57}$ $\overline{103}\ \overline{63}\ \overline{83}$
When Amberley retired: 4 wds.	$\overline{68}\ \overline{79}\ \overline{61}\ \overline{26}\ \overline{27}\ \overline{18}\ \overline{77}\ \overline{97}\ \overline{31}\ \overline{44}$ $\overline{45}\ \overline{95}\ \overline{87}$

Solution:

$\overline{1}\ \ \overline{2}\ \ \overline{3}\ \ \overline{4}\ \ \ \overline{5}\ \ \overline{6}\ \ \overline{7}\ \ \overline{8}\ \ \overline{9}\ \ \overline{10}\ \overline{11}\ \ \ \overline{12}\ \overline{13}\ \overline{14}\ \ \ \overline{15}\ \overline{16}\ \overline{17}\ \overline{18}\ \overline{19}\ \overline{20}\ \overline{21}\ \overline{22}\ \overline{23}\ \overline{24}$

$\overline{25}\ \overline{26}\ \overline{27}\ \overline{28}\ \ \ \overline{29}\ \overline{30}\ \overline{31}\ \overline{32}\ \ \overline{33}\ \overline{34}\ \overline{35}\ \overline{36}\ \ \ \overline{37}\ \overline{38}\ \overline{39}\ \overline{40}\ \ \ \overline{41}\ \overline{42}\ \overline{43}\ \ \ \overline{44}\ \overline{45}\ \overline{46}\ \overline{47}\ \overline{48}$

$\overline{49}\ \overline{50}\ \overline{51}\ \overline{52}\ \ \ \overline{53}\ \overline{54}\ \ \ \overline{55}\ \overline{56}\ \overline{57}\ \ \ \overline{58}\ \overline{59}\ \overline{60}\ \overline{61}\ \ \ \overline{62}\ \overline{63}\ \overline{64}\ \overline{65}\ \overline{66}\ \overline{67},\ \ \overline{68}\ \overline{69}\ \overline{70}$

$\overline{71}\ \overline{72}\ \overline{73}\ \overline{74}\ \overline{75}\ \overline{76}\ \overline{77}\ \overline{78}\ \overline{79}\ \ \ \overline{80}\ \overline{81}\ \overline{82}\ \overline{83}\ \ \ \ \overline{84}\ \overline{85}\ \overline{86}\ \overline{87}\ \overline{88}\ \overline{89}\ \overline{90}\ \overline{91}\ \overline{92}\ \overline{93}$

$\overline{94}\ \overline{95}\ \ \ \overline{96}\ \overline{97}\ \overline{98}\ \overline{99}\ \overline{100}\ \overline{101}\ \overline{102}\ \overline{103}$

Puzzler's Bonus

The Baker Street Irregulars
Crossword Puzzle

171. This puzzle was first published in *The Saturday Review of Literature,* May 19, 1934. Though it was signed "Mycroft Holmes," it is known to have been done by Frank V. Morley, an eminent early Baker Street Irregular. It is produced here by the kind permission of *The Saturday Review.* For some time, it was used as an entrance examination to the BSI, that most exalted of fan clubs.

ACROSS

1 A treatise on this, written at the age of twenty-one, had a European vogue and earned its author a professorship (2 words, 8,7)

8 It was of course to see these that Holmes enquired the way from Saxe-Coburg Square to the Strand (2 words, 10,5)

11 How the pips were set (2)

13 Not an Eley's No. 2 (which is an excellent argument with a gentleman who can twist steel pokers into knots) but the weapon in the tragedy of Birlstone (3)

14 What was done on the opposite wall in bullet-pocks by the patriotic Holmes (2)

15 What Watson recognized when he put his hand on Bartholomew Sholto's leg (5)

18 Where Watson met young Stamford, who introduced him to Sherlock Holmes (3)

20 A kind of pet, over which Dr. Grimesby Roylott hurled the local blacksmith (4)

21 Holmes should have said this before being so sure of catching the murderers of John Openshaw (2)

22 The kind of Pedro whence came the tiger (3)

23 Though he knew the methods, Watson sometimes found it difficult to do this (3)

25 Patron saint of old Mr. Farquhar's affliction and perhaps of Abe Slaney's men (5)

27 Perhaps a measure of Holmes's chemicals (2)

28 In short, Watson (2)

29 ⚔ ⚔ (2)

30 Curious that he did nothing in the night-time (3)

31 This would obviously not describe the empty house opposite 221B Baker Street (3)

34 It seems likely that Watson's elder brother suffered from this disease (2)

35 Though you might have taken this at Lodge 29, Chicago, nevertheless, you had to pass a test as well at Lodge 341, Vermissa (4)

37 The *Star* of Savannah (4)

40 Mrs. Barclay's reproach (in "The Crooked Man," of course) suggests the parable of this (3)

41 Scrawled in blood-red letters across the bare plaster at No. 3, Lauriston Gardens (5)

43 Holmes found this because he was looking for it in the muddy hollow where John Straker was killed (5)

44 Suggests Jonathan Small's leg (3)

45 The brother who left Watson no choice but to relate The Final Problem (2 words, 5,8)

DOWN

1 A country district in the west of England where "Cooee" was a common signal (2 words, 8,6)

2 Charles Augustus Milverton dealt with no niggard hand; therefore this would not describe him (4)

3 The kind of practice indulged by Mr. Williamson, the solitary cyclist's unfrocked clergyman— "there was a man of that name in orders whose career has been a singularly dark one" (3)

4 There is comparatively as much sense in Hafiz. Indeed, it's a case of identity (3 words, 2,2,6)

5 Caused the rift in the beryl coronet (3)

6 Many of Holmes's opponents had cause to (3)

7 Begins "Whose was it?" "His who is gone." "Who shall have it?" "He who will come" (2 words, 8,6)

9 Of four (4)

10 The number of Napoleons plus the number of the Randall gang (4)

12 One of the five sent "S.H. for J.O." (3)

16 To save the dying detective trouble, Mr. Chelverton [sic] Smith was kind enough to give the signal by turning this up (3)

17 The blundering constable who failed to gain his sergeant's stripes in the Lauriston Gardens Mystery (5)

19 One was mentioned by Boscombe Pool; yet it was illusory. There was a giant one of Sumatra; yet it was unwritten (3)

23 How Watson felt after "The Final Problem" (3)

24 He was epollicate (8)

26 Initials of the second most dangerous man in London (2)

32 Though Miss Mary Sutherland's boots were not unlike, they were really odd ones; the one having this slightly decorated, and the other plain (3)

33 You may forgive the plural form of these tobaccos, since Holmes smoked so much of them (5)

36 Behind this Black Jack of Ballarat waited and smoked an Indian cigar, of the variety which are rolled in Rotterdam (4)

38 and 39 The best I can make of these is the Latin for the sufferers of the epidemic which pleased Holmes so extremely that he said "A long shot, Watson, a very long shot," and pinched the Doctor's arm (4)

42 One of the two in the cardboard box (3)

44 Initials of the street in which Mycroft lodged (2)

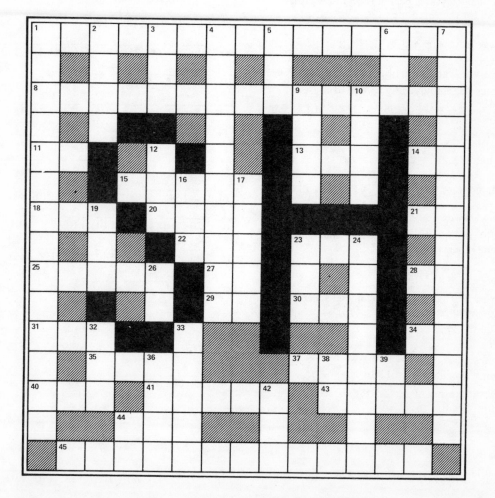

172. The Canon is complete. Farewell to the agony column, to the rascals, the rogues and the villains; to Lestrade and his cohorts; to the dancing men; the sly women; the secret societies; to the Master's brilliance and his Boswell's dumbfounded awe. The guilty have suffered; the innocent have been saved. But over it all, a brooding, multifaceted shadow casts a chilling pall on our delight. An overwhelming question hangs in the air, a question addressed by the following:

Clues

A "Come to ____," as Holmes's struggle with
Ms. Adler. . . . .
39 59 64 224 14 165

B Irne, until the idler was found . . . .
258 83 246 211 94 100 177 156

C "O, that this too too solid flesh would melt, ____,
and resolve itself into a dew!": Hamlet . . . .
166 115 136 232

D Learned person; scholar, as, occasionally, some
idiots . . . .
86 228 81 235 76 191

E The eighth letter of the Greek alphabet . . . .
139 204 179 147 247

F Vigor: 2 wds. (1034) . . . .
2 11 19 24 56 65 80 153 172 175
189 201 209 219 226 233 252

G What many a young person is on discovering
Homes for the first time . . . .
27 51 114 131 208 218 230 244 225 263

H He was "no means artist" (987) . . . .
188 30 3 66 210 98 236 181 106 171

I "____ out": absolute; obvious: 2 wds. . . . .
194 206 264 199 93 220

J Holmes was employed by several of these:
2 wds. . . . .
214 35 38 42 57 63 73 7 15 28
28 134 141 256

K See Letter X. . . . .
4 248 101 158 253 148 84 119 268 91

L Dull; monotonous . . . .
111 152 154 25

M Needy: 2 wds. (often with "of") . . . .
6 20 187 161 120 130

N Ability Holmes demonstrated in "Mazarin Stone"
among others: 3 wds. . . . .
16 29 82 128 180 198 196 261 250
140 95 174 17

O Company affected by "the colossal schemes of
Baron Maupertuis": Comp. (398) . . . .
12 21 34 41 62 70 96 118 155
212 217 50 168 183 237 137 89

P Insane; wrongheaded: Sl., 3 wds. . . . .
8 55 125 162 176 107 150 53 37 117

Q "The Adventure of ____," the shortest tale in the
Canon: 3 wds. . . . .
249 254 267 31 71 75 108 132 138
142 164 240 77 149 129

R A far cry from tomorrow morning . . . .
178 10 54 68 102 122 170 202 223
146 200

S Back and forth; rise and fall: 3 wds. 110 193 213 190 185 22 205 245 255 234

T See Letter X. 45 78 92 99 113 116 121 145 151

  160 182 186 207 222 227 242

U "The Adventure of the _____": it interrupted "the case of the Ferrers Documents": 2 wds. 109 9 32 79 90 123 241 40 46

  105 167 266

V Aisle; argument; scull. 36 251 216

W Loaded with action, as the Canon. 144 72 159 163 203 126 195 133

X With Letters K and T, the most frustrating and fascinating trio in the Canon (1095) 1 173 58 67 197 229 33 112 127 43

Y ". . . the rising young forger": Full name (623) . . .   18 26 48 61 69 85 104 231 260

  265 88 74 157 215 184

Z "_____ rave," like Dr. Grimesby Roylott: 2 wds. .   221 192 239 60 47 259 13

Z₁ Evened the odds, as Watson's revolver did so often .   143 87 23 124 5 243 135 257 52

Z₂ Wasted time, as Holmes never did along the way . .   44 238 103 49 262 169 97

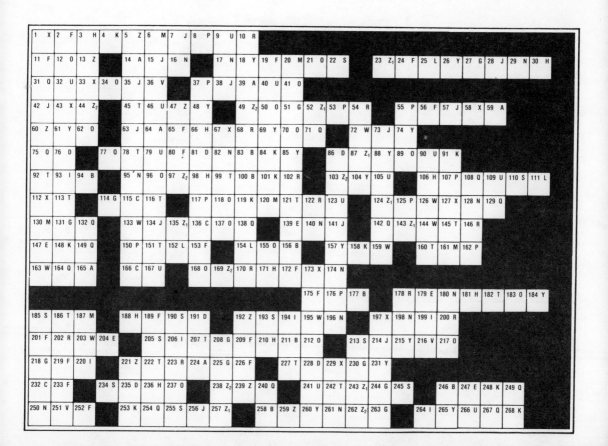

The Last Word

173.

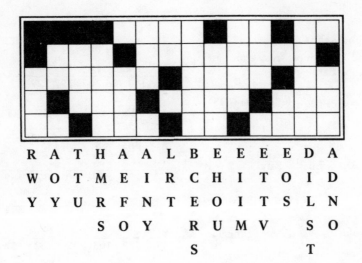

R A T H A A L B E E E E D A
W O T M E I R C H I T O I D
Y Y U R F N T E O I T S L N
    S O Y   R U M V   S O
           S   T

1.

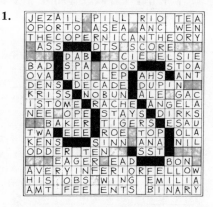

2. "HOW ON EARTH DID YOU KNOW THAT?" (18)

"There has been murder done, and the murderer was a man. He was more than six feet high, was in the prime of life, had small feet for his height, wore coarse, square-toed boots and smoked a Trichinopoly cigar. . . . These are only a few indications, but they may assist you." (32)

A	Holmes	M Disease
B	Oh, why	N Yesterday
C	Wheatfields	O Of Dimes
D	Of. March	P Undead
E	Norman Neruda	Q Keep the home
F	Erie	R Nothing better
G	Aortic aneurism	S Oasis
H	Rep	T Widow's woe
I	The Holy Four	U Torquay Terrace
J	Hath charms	V Halifax
K	Dissemble	W Afghanistan
L	Inter Gentes	X Tobias

3.

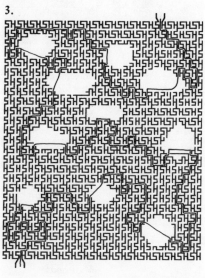

4. "There is nothing more unaesthetic than a policeman": T. Sholto (101)

5. "Women are never to be entirely trusted—not the best of them." (129)

6. "I never guess. It is a shocking habit—destructive to the logical faculty." (93)

7.

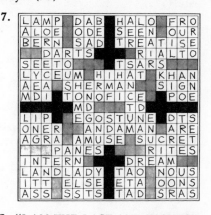

8. "I AM THE LAST AND HIGHEST COURT. . . ." (90)

"See how that one little cloud floats like a pink feather from some gigantic flamingo. Now the red rim of the sun pushes itself over the London cloudbank. It shines on a good many folk, but on none, I dare bet, who are on a stranger errand than you and I." (121)

A	Irregulars	N Hawk-like
B	An automaton	O Indian-lunkah
C	Monographs	P GWTW
D	Tiffs	Q High Noon
E	Hypodermic	R Eftsoon
F	Euclid	S Sholto
G	Le Villard	T Toe men
H	Athelney	U Creosote
I	Stagnation	V Of Four
J	The Sidhe	W Unfed
K	A bender	X Rebel foe
L	No, No, Nanette	Y Timon's
M	Dost Akbar	

9. "To Sherlock Holmes she is always *the* woman." (161)

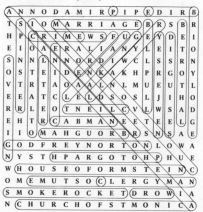

10. "YOU DON'T MIND BREAKING THE LAW?" (169)

And that was how a great scandal threatened to affect the kingdom of Bohemia, and how the best plans of Mr. Sherlock Holmes were beaten by a woman's wit. He used to make merry over the cleverness of women, but I have not heard him do it of late. (175)

A Yankee Doodle
B Off the wall
C Upshot
D Dhow
E Offenbach
F Nome
G The Toast of the
H Mrs. Turner
I IFOH
J New Wave
K Dammed
L Bohemian
M Rashomon
N East is
O Adverts
P Kramm
Q Irene Adler
R Navy boat
S Gasogene
T Trincomalee
U How the West
V Ebb tide
W Latch
X Attacks
Y Whether

11.

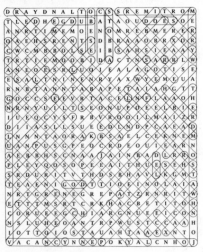

"L'homme C'est rien—L'oeuvre c'est tout." (190)

12.

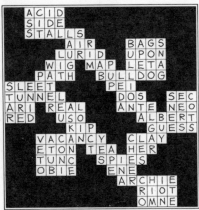

13.

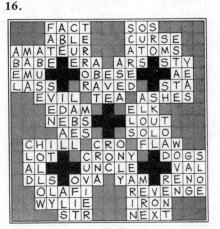

1. "Perhaps I have trained myself to see what others overlook." (192)

2. "There is as much sense in Hafiz as in Horace, and as much knowledge of the world." (201)

14. "There is nothing more deceptive than an obvious fact." (204)

15. "Why does fate play such tricks with poor, helpless worms?" (217)

16.

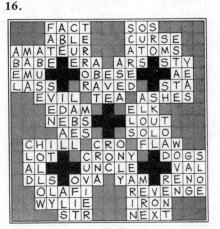

17.
Lee	Major Freebody
Paramore	Sherlock Holmes
John Swain	Grice Patersons
John Watson	Major Prendergast
John Openshaw	Col. Elias Openshaw

18.
Uffa	Tennessee
Sussex	Pondicherry
Horsham	East London
Florida	The Carolinas
Savannah	Waterloo Bridge

19.
Pip	Sundial
Keys	Mail-boat
Cable	Lone Star
Rifle	Albert Dock
Estate	Green-scummed pool

20. ". . . a trusty comrade is always of use; and a chronicler still more so." (233) "You have a grand gift of silence, Watson. It makes you quite invaluable." (233)

21. "I confess that I have been as blind as a mole, but it is better to learn wisdom late than never to learn it at all." (241)

22. "I deserve to be kicked from here to Charing Cross." (240)

23.

1. "Who would think that so pretty a toy would be a purveyor to the gallows and the prison." (249)

2. "I am not retained by the police to supply their deficiencies." (257)

24. "Chance has put in our way a most singular and whimsical problem." (257)

25. "There is the making of a very pretty villain in you." (255)

26. Found at the corner of Goodge Street a goose and a black felt hat. (249)

27.

| L | A | S | T | | | A | D | V | T | | S | T | R | A | P |

(crossword grid)

28.

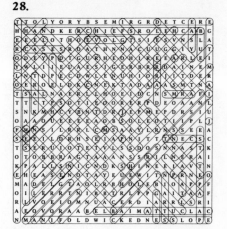

"The deadliest snake in India" (272)

29.

30. "We can't command our love, but we can our actions." (298)

31. "I will tell you the true solution. . . .Lady St. Simon is a myth." (296)

32. "I read nothing except the criminal news and the agony column." (288)

33. "IT IS A VERY SWEET LITTLE PROBLEM. . . ." (312)

"I do not know what I have done to be so severely tried. . . .Only two days ago I was a happy and prosperous man, without a care in the world. Now I am left to a lonely and dishonoured age. One sorrow comes close upon the heels of another. My niece, Mary, has deserted me." (312)

A Intention
B Thoroughly
C Idea
D Sea salt
E Arthur Holder
F Vetoes
G Escapade
H Rashomon
I Your loving Mary
J Soft-shoe
K Wayward
L Easy-chair
M Epsom Downs
N Thirty-nine
O Lown down
P Idée
Q Threadneedle
R The Spy
S Laocoon
T Eftsoons
U Poop deck
V Rae
W One
X Bow-window
Y Lame
Z Emanate
Z₁ Moué

34.

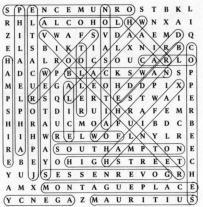

35. "The lowest and vilest alleys in London do not present a more dreadful record of sin than does the smiling and beautiful countryside." (323)

36.

People	Places
1. Sherlock Holmes	1. Baker Street
2. Violet Hunter	2. Copper Beeches
3. Spence Munro	3. Black Swan Hotel
4. Alice Rucastle	4. Philadelphia
5. Jephro Rucastle	5. Montague Street
6. Miss Stoper	6. Winchester
7. John Watson	7. Southampton Road
8. Edward Rucastle	8. Hampshire

37. "I have devised seven separate explanations, each of which would cover the facts as far as we know them." (323)

38.

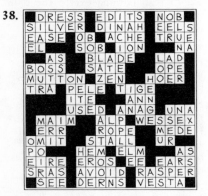

39. Silver Blaze should have won your Wessex Cup II by one length over Pugilist and Desborough, by two over The Negro, three over Rasper, and four over the sluggish Iris. Answers:
I. 1. Cigar; 2. Maple*ton*—negative answer correct; 3. It was red and black; 4. It was over £30 (£37/15, actually); 5. Holmes complained of Gregory's *lack* of imagination; 6. Three sheep went lame.

II. 1. Gregory; 2. Silas Brown; 3. Simpson; 4. Holmes; 5. Hunter; 6. Watson.
III. 1. Edith; 2. Iris; 3. Straker's; 4. Blaze.

40. "SO MUCH FOR AFTERNOON WALKS." (351)

"Watson," said he, "if it should ever strike you that I am getting a little overconfident in my powers, or giving less pains to a case than it deserves, kindly whisper 'Norbury' in my ear, and I shall be infinitely obliged to you." (362)

A Synapse	M Edison
B Opinion	N Reseat
C Misty	O Neighbourly
D Urbane	P Overwhelming
E Countrified	Q Oats
F Hop merchant	R Nasal
G Florist	S Wideawake
H Overriding	T Aides
I Revisiting	U Livid tint
J Alehouse	V Kettle
K Fly-by-night	W Stylist
L Today	

41. "Effie loves me. Don't let there be any mistake about that." (353)

42. "Trust me, Jack," she cried. "Trust me only this once." (357)

43. "This is John Hebron, of Atlanta, and a nobler man never walked the earth." (361)

44.

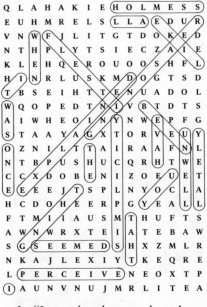

1. "I perceive that you have been unwell lately." (363)

2. Like all Holmes's reasoning the thing seemed simplicity itself when it was once explained. (363)

45. "Now you see the point about the handwriting." (372)

46. "My God," cried our client, "what a blind beetle I've been." (372)

47. Answer: "You only have to read the story and you'll solve this code."
Solution: This is the "Gloria Scott" code, where you read every third word, beginning with the first.

48. Answer: "This one won't be so easy."
Solution: The first letter of each word forms the code message. (With thanks to V. Nabokov.)

49. Answer: "Actually, I'm playing with you."
Solution: Reverse the order of the first two letters, the second two, the third two, etc.

50. Answer: "Proudly presenting you:"
Solution: In the first word, the first letter of the alphabet is assigned the number "1" and the alphabet is numbered from 1 to 26. In the second word, the first letter is number 2 and the alphabet is numbered to 26 and "Z" is numbered "1." In the third word, the progression is advanced one more.

51. Answer: "More Codes Later"
Solution: This code bears a passing resemblance to the one we will encounter in "The Valley of Fear." The initial letter pairs stand for all the stories in this book thus far which have either a crossword puzzle or an acrostic (or both) representing them. SS= A Study in Scarlet, SF= The Sign of Four, etc. SB1, 2, and 3, of course, are A Scandal in Bohemia, The Speckled Band, and Silver Blaze respectively. The number after the initials represents the square to look for. If it's in a crossword puzzle, you will have to count either down (D) or across (A), not counting the numbered square, to discover the letter sought. If it's in an acrostic, the number alone represents the space in which you wrote the letter you want. Slashes separate letters.

52. "IT WAS THE END OF THE *GLORIA SCOTT.*" (385)
"Now, you don't think it likely that a man who could do anything is going to wear his breeches out sitting in the stinking hold of a rat-gutted, beetle-ridden, mouldy old coffin of a Chin China coaster. . . . Such a man will look after himself and . . . his chums." (382)

A Identities
B Tongue
C Wild-duck
D Annoyance
E Sham
F Tooth
G Hiccoughing
H Edward Holly
I Eight-knot
J Nodes
K Dead with
L Only friend
M Float
N Thumb
O Harness cask
P Enigmatical
Q Ghoulish
R Leis
S Ohioan
T Ruffian
U Imminent
V Ad Hoc
W Show Boat
X Cuff links
Y Otter
Z Try to
Z_1 Till

53.

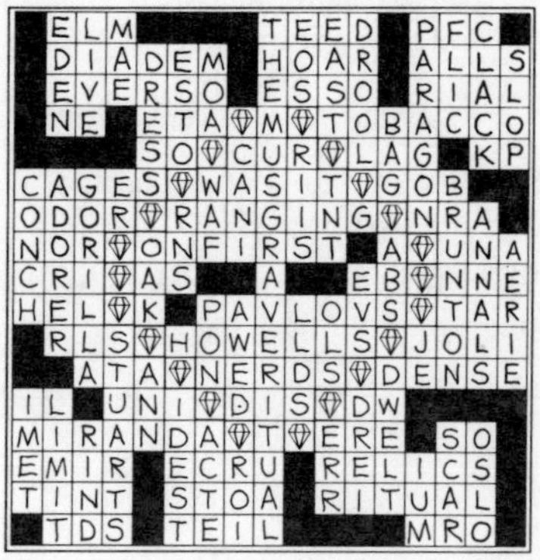

54.

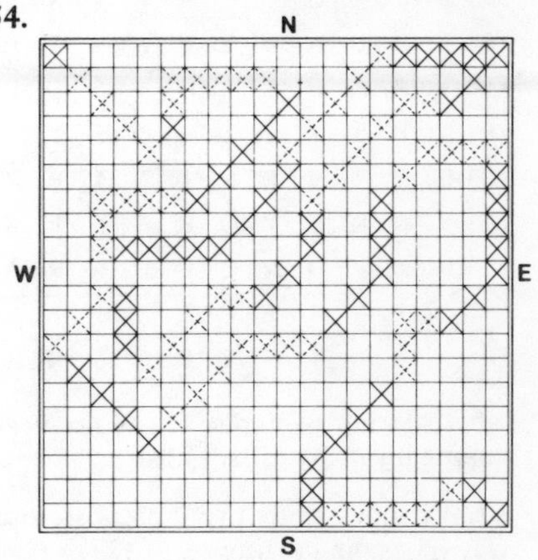

Note: The different markings indicate the changes in direction taken, question by question.

Answers: 1. Tobacco; 2. ____ 3. Mountains of documents; 4. Tin; 5. ____; 6. Club-foot; 7. Oil-stained cloth; 8. Montague Street; 9. ____; 10. Reginald; 11. Hurlstone; 12. 20 years; 13. ____; 14. Café noir; 15. Over the oak; 16. 64 feet; 17. Brunton's muffler; 18. Rachel Howells; 19. ____; 20. None of the above (they were hidden *after* Charles I's execution, during the Civil War, before Charles II's restoration); 21. Second; 22. ____.

55. "It is of the highest importance in the art of detection to be able to recognize, out of a number of facts, which are incidental and which vital." (407)

56. a. "I have usually found that there was method in his madness." (402)

b. My poor friend's face had suddenly assumed the most dreadful expression. (403)

c. I was pained at the mistake, for I knew how keenly Holmes would feel any slip of the kind. (404)

57. 1. Baron Maupertuis
2. Colonel Hayter
3. Old Acton
4. Forrester
5. Alec Cunningham
6. Old Cunningham
7. William Kirwan
8. Annie Morrison (read backward)

58. "I have no doubt Jackson would take my practice." (412)

59. "But when one gets old, one has a longing for home." (421)

60. "Excellent!" I cried. "Elementary," said he. (412)

61.

```
A H T E M A N S O I E Y
S N T F O P L A C E X J
S F O U N D E N A S I H
E T E A H I L O M S U R
R D F T T B L A O S E C
U O T I Z E N I N I R T
T Y G R G Y O R G H V K
A H X P D N Q U D W R A
N O I T A I C E R P P A
U F L A I E T B N S H T
```

Appreciation of nature found no place among his many gifts. (423)

62. "It does seem a very preposterous way of settling a dispute." (423)

63. "My own hobby has always been nervous disease." (425)

64. "Art in the blood is liable to take the strangest forms." (435)

65. "Sherlock has all the energy of the family," said Mycroft. (442)

66. "HOW COMES IT THAT HE IS UNKNOWN?" (435)

"I said that he was my superior in observation and deduction. . . . But he has no ambition and no energy. He will not even go out of his way to verify his own solutions, and would rather be considered wrong than take the trouble to prove himself right." (436)

A	How now brown	N	Thigh
B	Observation	O	Hooded
C	Whitehall	P	Eleven
D	Cobbler	Q	In tune to
E	Off guard	R	Seven years
F	Misanthropy	S	Unsociable
G	Edit	T	Nervous malady
H	Sophy	U	Kratides
I	Inhuman	V	Nourished
J	Tug of war	W	Orion
K	Ten	X	Writhe
L	Hittite	Y	Negotiations
M	At odds		

67.

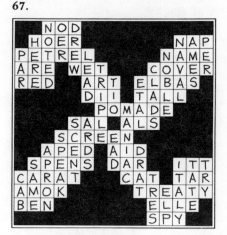

68. 1. Mrs. Tanguey
2. Percy Phelps
3. Charles Gorot
4. Lord Holdhurst
5. Annie Harrison
6. Joseph Harrison
7. Monsieur Dubugue
8. Fritz von Waldbaum

69. 1. Italy
2. Ripley
3. Surrey
4. England
5. Waterloo
6. Northumberland
7. Briarbrae, Woking
8. Clapham Junction

70. 1. Bedroom
2. Brain-fever
3. Litmus-paper
4. Naval treaty
5. Bunsen burner
6. Foreign Office
7. Triple Alliance
8. Coldstream Guards

71. "Ay, there's the genius and the wonder of the thing!" (470)

72. "He sits motionless, like a spider in the centre of its web. . . ." (471)

73. . . . the best and the wisest man whom I have ever known. (480)

74.

```
J O B S   O S C A R   A J A R
U N I T   B U O N O   C O C O
M O N A   I M B E D   T U E S
P R O B L E M   R E C O R D S
    M S S   I N G   E R N
M C I     T O Y     A G A
A L A S         B L O B
T E L E         E D D Y
C A T E         L E O S
H R H     L E E     G T S
    E E R   E E L   O P E
S L O W E S T   D E F E N C E
H E R E   O T T E R   T E A L
O V E R   F E A R S   E V I L
T I M S   A R O S E   R E N E
```

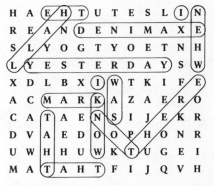

A Twice-told tale	N Incredulity
B Huntsman	O Khartoum
C Inconceivable	P Evil
D Stakes	Q The Holy War
E Imminent	R Humor
F Shock	S Estimated
G In jest	T Of Maynooth
H No votes	U Lips
I Dis	V Dogged
J Easy-going	W Doffs
K Edith	X Abominable
L Dust to dust	Y Yawl
M Lath	Z Slush

75. THE BEST AND THE WISEST MAN (480)

"...Moriarty...awaits my convenience.... I am pleased to think that I shall be able to free society from any further effects of his presence, though I fear that it is at a cost which will give pain to my friends, and especially, my dear Watson, to you." (479)

A Thrust-and-parry	L Hattie
B Hereditary	M Efficacy
C Ecclesiastic	N Woo
D Binomial theorem	O Impishly
E Effectively	P Sweat
F Stowaway	Q Events
G Third of May	R Sui
H Alpine-stock	S Thais
I Nurse	T Marylebone
J Death	U Antagonist
K The Flight of	V Napoleon of crime

76.

```
                    M C I
    C E D E         O L A
    O L E O         R U N
S T A K E S         A B S
H O L E     D Y A N S
O R T     A P E A R
T E A T   S E C R E T
    R O N A L D A D A I R
    R E G A R D   M E W S
    C A N O E     T E T
  O A K S T       A R T E
M S G       A R R E S T
I C E       L A M A
C A N       L E S T
A R T
```

77. "THIS IS, INDEED, LIKE THE OLD DAYS." (486)

"With five volumes you could just fill that gap on that second shelf. It looks untidy, does it not, sir?"

I moved my head to look at the cabinet behind me. When I turned again, Sherlock Holmes was standing smiling at me across my study table. (485)

78.

```
H A (E H) T U T E S L (I) N
R E/A/N (D E N I M A X E) E
S/L/Y O G T Y O E T N H
(L/Y E S T E R D A Y) S W
X D L B X (I)(W) T K I F E
A C (M A R K) A Z A E R/O
C A T A E (N) S I J E/K R
D V A E D O O P H O N R
U W H H U W K (T) U G E I
M A (T A H T) F I J Q V H
```

"I know that that mark was not there when I examined the hall yesterday." (507)

79.

1. Verner	8. Holmes
2. Moriarty	9. Cornelius
3. Watson	10. Stevens
4. Murillo	11. Lexington
5. Oldacre	12. Hyams
6. McFarlane	13. Lestrade
7. Graham	

80. "I was engaged to him, Mr. Holmes, when I heard a shocking story of how he had turned a cat loose in an aviary, and I was so horrified at his brutal cruelty that I would have nothing more to do with him." (503)

81. Answer: "Again, an easy one to begin."

Solution: See our story.

82. Answer: "Now one that will challenge."

Solution: Add full upright lines to the ones provided.

NOW ONE THAT WILL CHALLENGE

83. Answer: "You can solve this puzzle: Why did the chicken cross the road?"

Solution: This is my "More or Less Opposites" code. Each word is more or less the opposite of the one sought for, though the opposites, perforce, need to be rather fanciful at times.

84.

84. Answer: "Maybe this one's too easy."

Solution: Developed from the parlor game "Rasputin," this code employs the first letter only of each name used. The "bangs" indicate vowels to be inserted. The number of bangs corresponds to the usual order of presenting vowels, i.e., A, E, I, O, U. A=1 bang; E=2 bangs, etc. The run of vowels toward the end adds a tiny *divertissement* following the solution's initial hurdle.

85.

85. Answer: "More codes in the Valley."

Solution: The first two letters of the simple answers to the definitions are run together for the code answer. The answers to the definitions are: MOtion—REady—COrrect—DEath—SImple—NTh—HEaven—VAcation—LLama—EYes.

86. "You will excuse me, I am sure. It is my business. ..." (527)

87. "He is a perfect gentleman. But a girl always knows." (530)

88. "I emerged as you see me. Mr. Woodley went home in a cart." (532)

89.

```
A M O A N T B E Y Z E A O L U Y
U E P H U T M Y S E L F X I I
P L J V E G D X I T I F M V I W
T A D K S R N J W G I H A O M G
H A Q T E F A O I N F G Y I N O
T T P B C A S W S E E V C I D B
Z R R C E A B N A T U E T X H J
S Y X O E W I V E U A S T A S E
V B E Q N H N O T E E W V D H C
W O E L S R T O H R S E E H H T
P O I T P N A O E M N L K E J K
U D H T I I N T G A I T I R N S
G F S R E S N S I D N C L M H B
L T E H T I I D H O U N D S G A
X X C S T J J L K T Y T L Z E A
R E O T I W A O V H U F E Z V N
S M N E Q R O T W A L B U H F U
U K D R E S C E N T E Q D M P Z
Y B O A P H L O M I N I N L O O
Q J D S E I T I P S N I N H O H
E P E R H A P S K S O O F H G C
C E D R P C A O B Q L I T S O A
```

1. "Perhaps the scent is not so cold but that two old hounds like Watson and myself may get a sniff of it." (543)
2. "It is the second most interesting object that I have seen in the north." (558)

90.

```
A R G E N T I N E S P E A R S X I
L C H A I R O P E T E R C A R E Y
L I Q K M T P U R I T A N C E S S
A F S T A N L E Y H O P K I N S E
R I T A H E T R E L A E S V M U A
D C A A A L A N O S L I W I C W S N
Y P N C A B I O H A R P O O N D I
E A N C S D I A Y A C H T R O N E C
S A S A X O N N T E Y K S T R E O R
L I O S L A T E R P L U P S T T R
A D S T H G I L D N A L T E H S N
R A T I S N R I A C K C I R T A P
Y N U W E P I G E N R A Y O A E Y
H A H U G H P A T T I N S F P E R
G C W A G E S N T H D E C K E U
N M A R S S T C O S T A R I C A F
I L E T O H E Y T E L B M A R B E
D E E L S N A M D O O W A T C H R
```

"I am the pupil and you are the Master." (570)

91. "If I killed Black Peter, the law should give me thanks. ..." (571)

92. "One should always look for a possible alternative." (567)

93. "When do we start." "You are not coming." "Then you are not going." (576)

94. "... it would be amusing if we ended by sharing the same cell." (577)

95. "Take that, you hound—and that! —and that!—and that!—and that!" (580)

96.

97.

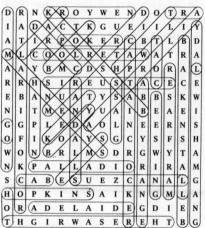

It was at such moments that for an instant he ceased to be a reasoning machine and betrayed his human love for admiration and applause. (594)

98. "The press, Watson, is a most valuable institution, if you only know how to use it." (590)

99.

1. Gelder and Co.	A. Kennington Road
2. Morse Hudson	B. High Street
3. Dr. Barnicot	C. Stepney
4. Horace Harker	D. Lower Brixton Road
5. Harding Brothers	E. Kensington
6. Josiah Brown	F. Reading
7. Mr. Sandeford	G. Chiswick

1C; 2A; 3D; 4E; 5B; 6G; 7F.

100. "I gave him a little brandy and left him collapsed in a chair." (597)

101. "He had no warning until you were at the very door." (600)

102. "Gilchrist got his blue for the hurdle and the long jump." (600)

103. IT WAS A WILD, TEMPESTUOUS NIGHT. (607)

"Ah! I am only a student—a man of dreams. I cannot explain the practical things of life. But still, we are aware, my friend, that love-gages may take strange shapes. By all means take another cigarette. It is a pleasure to see anyone appreciate them so." (616)

A Inference	G Watch-chain
B Tate	H Impatience
C Willoughby Smith	I Lease
D Amity	J Deer
E Salad	K Toyota
F Asea	L Explanation
	M Mrs. Marker

N Palimpsest	T Ukase
O Every fortnight	U Stanley
P Seabee	V Near East
Q Tarlton	W IATSE
R Uppingham	X Garden gate
S Once	Y Half a loaf
	Z Toast

104. "I'll have the plate moved over to the bank this evening." (627)

105. "They say he could chalk his billiard-cue with his knuckles." (624)

106. "Your reflection, though profound, had already crossed my mind." (626)

107.

"Not guilty, my lord," said I. (650)

108. "Come, Watson, come!" he cried. "The game is afoot."

109. "How could I leave her in the power of this madman?" (649)

110. *Vox populi, vox Dei.* You are acquitted, Captain Crocker." (650)

111. "She comes of a caste who do not lightly show emotion." (657)

112. "Good Lord, sir!" he cried, with amazement on his face. (662)

113. "Come, sir," said he. "There is more in this than meets the eye." (666)

114. "THAT IS A HARD SAYING, MR. HOLMES." (653)

"You are two of the most busy men in the country," said he, "and in my own small way I have also a good many calls upon me. I regret exceedingly that I cannot help you in this matter, and any continuation of this interview would be a waste of time." (652)

A Trelawney Hope	E Indefatigable
B Hottentot	F Sussex Downs
C Acumen	G At one with
D Twain	H Hootenanny
	I Await

115. "I HAVE BEEN CONSCIOUS OF SHADOWS. . . ." (711)

At every turn Baskerville gave an exclamation of delight, looking eagerly about him and asking countless questions. To his eyes all seemed beautiful, but to me a tinge of melancholy lay upon the countryside, which bore so clearly the mark of the waning year. (700)

116.

117.

118. "I HAVE BEEN IN THE VALLEY OF FEAR." (796)

Three centuries had flowed past the old Manor House, centuries of births and of homecomings, of country dances and of the meetings of fox hunters. Strange that now in its old age this dark business should have cast its shadow upon the venerable walls! (787)

119. Answer: "By no means will you need much time to master this first one. Excellent!"

Solution: Again, the code is based on the one found in our story. Instead of *Whitaker's Almanac*, however, the book you needed to solve this one is the Doubleday edition of the complete Sherlock Holmes. On page "549" of that volume (the first number in the code), you will find that the word "By" (the first word in the answer) is in the 42nd line, the 3rd word ("42/3" in the code). "No" is in the 3rd line, the 9th word ("3/9"), etc.

120. Answer: "Beside number two the first one's nothing."

Solution: I am saying, of course, that Code #1 was much easier to figure out than this one, #2. It's what's inside the boxes that counts. In the first box, the B side (or "BESIDE") is indicated. The second box has a numeral two ("number two") in it. The next three, joined by brackets, invite you to deduce "the first ones" which needs to be repunctuated for the answer ("one's"). And there's "nothing" in the last box.

121. Answer: "But we must not abandon codes for rebuses."

Solution: Shift the first letter of each group of nonsense words to the end of the group preceding it, making sure to close the "circle" by moving the first letter ("R") around to the end of the last group. Then spell out each resulting group backwards and *voilà!*

122. Answer: "Here's my pièce de résistance:"

Solution: Arrange each group of five characters in vertical columns next to

one another. This forms the "squarely" of the hint. Then, starting in the middle, read outward in a spiral, counterclockwise ("against time").

123. Answer: "Hi (if you spelled out "Ed," you're on the wrong track), Pal: (See?) No more codes, OK? And thanks for buying my book. DC (Me)

Solution: The "Valley of Fear" Double-Crostic is the *Whitaker's Almanac* you need to solve this cipher. The numbers in the code *outside* the parentheses correspond to the letter designation printed (along with that number) in the Double-Crostic square. The numbers in the code *inside* the parentheses correspond to the letter *you* wrote in that numbered square while solving the puzzle. My "signature" works with either system, spelling out DC in the nonparenthetical scheme and "Me" in the other.

124.

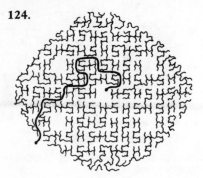

125.

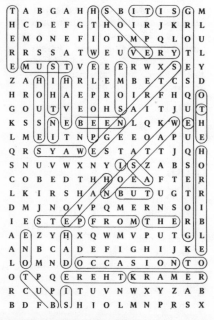

1. "It is grotesque, Watson, but as I have had occasion to remark, there is but one step from the grotesque to the horrible." (887-88)

2. ". . . there must have been some very strange people with some very strange ways in this house." (879)

126.

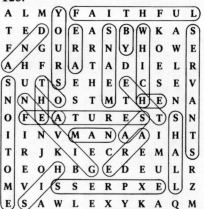

"The features are given to a man as the means by which he shall express his emotions, and yours are faithful servants." (889)

127. "I thought more of my wife's footmark in the mud than I did of her whole body and soul." (898)

128. "What object is served by this circle of misery? . . ." (901)

129. "Dear me!" said he, turning over the pages, "what a chorus of groans, cries, and bleatings! What a rag-bag of singular happenings." (904)

130. "Education never ends, Watson. It is a series of lessons with the greatest for the last." (907)

131. "I have a great fancy to see this lodger of yours, Mrs. Warren." (905)

132. "Surely Jimmy will not break his mother's heart." (904)

133.

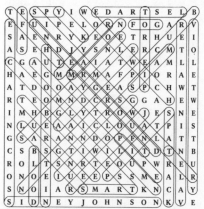

"I play the game for the game's own sake." (917)

134. "A COOLIE DISEASE FROM SUMATRA." (933)

"You won't fail me. You never did fail me. No doubt there are natural enemies which limit the increase of the creatures. You and I, Watson, we have done our part. Shall the world, then, be overrun by oysters? No, no; horrible! You'll convey all that is in your mind." (936)

A A noble mind
B Culverton Smith
C Our Town
D Of Thee
E Landlady
F Infallibly
G Everyone
H Dr. Ainstree
I Is but a child
J Superhero
K Event
L Authority
M Sweety
N Enow
O Foolish child
P Rotherhithe
Q One on one
R Malodorous
S Sewerman
T Uncharitable
U Muni
V Aye aye
W Turvy
X Rowe
Y A rut

135. "His particular specialty is the beguiling of lonely ladies." (947)

136. "Scotland Yard feels lonely without me, and it causes an unhealthy excitement among the criminal classes." (943)

137.

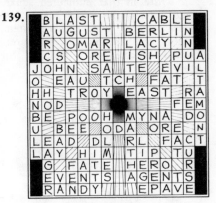

Vague shapes swirled and swam amid the dark cloud-bank each a menace and a warning of something coming, the advent of some unspeakable dweller upon the threshold, whose very shadow would blast my soul. (965)

138.

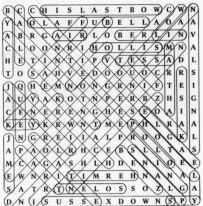

"Good old Watson!" (980)

139.

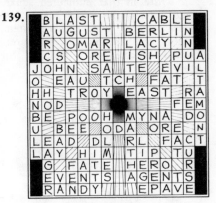

For God and Country

140. "BLOODY HANDS AND LECHEROUS LIPS." (992)

One eye was already white and glazed. The other was red and inflamed. The features which I had admired a few minutes before were now like some beautiful painting over which the artist has passed a wet and foul sponge. They were blurred, discoloured, inhuman, terrible. (998)

A Baron Adelbert Gruner
B Lazy
C Oriental
D Okra
E Duff
F Yachting
G Household
H Amusement
I News-sheet
J Debate
K September third
L And thrash the hide
M Newsie
N Dada
O Law west of
P Effete
Q Chin
R Hideaway
S Eire
T Rewipe
U Outfield
V Underworld
W Souse
X Larue
Y I love him
Z Peace and Wainwright
Z_1 Swami

141.

People

James Dodd
Colonel Emsworth
Old Ralph
Mr. Kent

Baldy Simpson
Anderson
Sir James Saunders

Places	Things
Middlesex	Boer War
Throgmorton Street	Elephant gun
	Tapestry
Tuxbury Old Park	Voyage
South Africa	Cheese
Pretoria	Weeklies
Bedfordshire	Leper
Buffelsspruit	

142. Alas, that I should have to show my hand so when I tell my own story! (1007-8)

"I see no more than you, but I have trained myself to notice what I see." (1000)

143. "It is my business to know things. That is my trade." (1008)

144. "We all have neglected opportunities to deplore." (1016)

145. "No violence, I beg of you! Consider the furniture!" (1021)

146.
1. Count Negretto Sylvius
2. Mazarin Stone
3. Sam Merton
4. Lord Cantlemere
5. Straubenzee
6. Ikey Sanders
7. Prime Minister
8. Home Secretary
9. Sherlock Holmes

147. Hidden Phrase: The lady had come ... to that time of life when even the proudest beauty finds the half light more welcome. (1031)
Leftover Quotation: "I, of course, was the wolf; he the lamb." (1033)

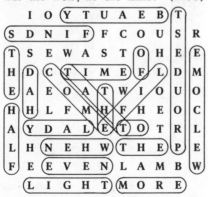

148. "There are always some lunatics about. It would be a dull world without them." (1027)

149. "Don't play with me, Mr. Holmes. It is too terribly serious." (1039)

150. "I fear that there is pain for you, Mr. Ferguson. . . ." (1040)

151. "His very soul is consumed with hatred for this splendid child. . . ." (1043)

152. "THE WORLD IS BIG E-NOUGH FOR US." (1034)

Ferguson was standing by the bed, choking, his hands outstretched and quivering. "This, I fancy, is the time for our exit, Watson," said Holmes in a whisper. "If now you will take one elbow of the too faithful Dolores, I will take the other." (1044)

A	Twisted	L	Into the crowd
B	Have a right to	M	Giant Rat
C	Equine	N	Eiffel
D	Whiff	O	Nosh
E	Oh yes she will	P	Ordinarily
F	Rebus of a cheese	Q	Unfold
G	Look to't	R	Gramps
H	Doxy	S	Hath thee
I	Ill-used woman	T	Fobs
J	Situation	U	Ohio
K	Biting his neck	V	Rawest
		W	Unkind
		X	Stew

153. It was worth a wound—it was worth many wounds—to know the depth of loyalty and love which lay behind that cold mask. (1053)

154. It may have been comedy or it may have been tragedy. (1044)

155. "What we wanted at present was just your sweet self." (1054)

156. ". . . this crazy boob of a bug-hunter with the queer name. . . ." (1054)

157. A BATTERED TIN DISPATCH-BOX (1054)

A third case worthy of note is that of Isadora Persano, the well-known journalist and duellist, who was found stark staring mad with a match box in front of him which contained a remarkable worm said to be unknown to science. (1055)

A	Alicia	N	Injustice
B	Backward	O	Swoon
C	Admit that	P	Phillimore
D	Thankless	Q	Accursed
E	This woman	R	Two for the show
F	Eftsoon	S	Counts
G	Rune	T	Harshly
H	Eat of a king	U	Batman and Robin
I	Danke	V	Otto
J	Thor Mere	W	Xantho
K	Inward life		
L	No windows		
M	Dwarf		

158. I was a whetstone for his mind. I stimulated him. (1071)

159. ". . . the wolfhound no doubt disapproved of the financial bargain." (1075)

160. "What sort of cesspool may not our poor world become?" (1083)

161. Hidden Phrase: "Pangs shot through the chest, causing me to fall as if struck by a bullet." (1094)
Leftover Quotation: I, my old housekeeper, and my bees have the estate all to ourselves. (1083)

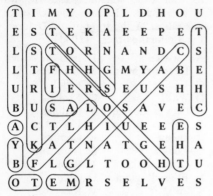

162. He seemed to live in some high, abstract region of surds. ... (1084)

163. "Cyanea!" I cried. "Cyanea! Behold the Lion's Mane!" (1093)

164. "The ways of fate are indeed hard to understand. If there is not some compensation hereafter, then the world is a cruel jest." (1101)

165. "The example of patient suffering is in itself the most precious of all lessons to an impatient world." (1101)

166. "Your life is not your own," he said. "Keep your hands off it." (1101)

167. Holmes held up his hand in a gesture of pity and protest. (1102)

168.
1. Mummy
2. Sam Brewer
3. John Mason
4. Norman Hugos
5. Josiah Barnes
6. Grand National
7. Shoscombe Prince
8. Shoscombe Old Place
9. Sir Robert Norberton
10. Lady Beatrice Falder

169. "It was all in order, sir, except that in one corner was a bit of a human body." (1105)

170. "I can picture you whispering soft nothings with the young lady at the Blue Anchor, and receiving hard somethings in exchange." (1116)

171.

172. NUTS! "THE WORLD IS NOT YET PREPARED."

Phillimore
And his damned umbrella (1054),
Victor Lynch (1034)
And that Dundas fella (191),
The furniture van
In Grosvenor Square (288),
And Aldridge, who helped
In the laundry affair (897),
The lizard (1034), the leech (607),
The worm (1055) and the rat (1034),
Not to mention the Yeggman (1034)—
Now what about that?
With furrowed brows
And ragged nails,
We wait and still wait
For those untold tales.

A Naught
B Unwedded
C Thaw
D Savant
E Theta
F Hammersmith wonder
G Enthralled
H Wainwright
I Out and
J Royal families
K Lighthouse
L Drab
M In want
N Sleight of hand
O Netherland-Sumatra
P Off the wall
Q The Veiled Lodger
R Yesternight
S Ebb and flow
T Trained cormorant
U Priory School
V Row
W Eventful
X Politician
Y Arthur H. Staunton
Z Rant and
Z_1 Equalized
Z_2 Dawdled

173. "... file it in our archives, Watson. Some day the true story may be told." (1122)

Diagramless Starting Boxes:
Puzzle #12: 3rd box
Puzzle #67: 3rd box
Puzzle #76: 12th box
Puzzle #116: 4th box